BUILDING YOUR OWN BOAT

1. Fairey Marine Firefly

BUILDING YOUR OWN BOAT

GRAHAM BELL

LONDON
METHUEN & CO LTD
36 ESSEX STREET · STRAND · WC2

CATALOGUE NO. 6006/U

Printed and bound in Great Britain by
Jarrold & Sons Ltd. Norwich

PREFACE

In writing this book I have purposely narrowed the field of possibilities. I have not included canoes because they are a specialized class, and there are many excellent books on the subject. Fibreglass is also outside the scope of this book. It undoubtedly has a great future, and development is going ahead at a great pace; but there is one major snag – a mould is required and this can be expensive in cost and labour, particularly if only one boat is to be built from it. For this reason fibreglass does not compete with marine ply in amateur construction; but the situation may soon change. If any readers would like to try their hand at fibreglass, either for building a hull or some fittings, I will gladly supply the names of suitable firms dealing in the material.

I have also omitted any mention of Catamarans because they are still in an early stage of development. At the end of 1957 a number of 'Cats' were available as finished boats or in kit form. Many of the details of construction described in this book apply as much to Catamarans as to the conventional types.

Development of all types of small boats is pressing on at a tremendous rate. It is virtually impossible to keep a book of this sort up to date, in spite of all the help I have received from firms in the industry.

Finally I would like to thank most sincerely all those who answered my endless questions so patiently, particularly Mr D. W. Pollock of The Bell Woodworking Co. I must make it clear at this point that, in spite of my name, I am in no way connected with this famous Leicester firm. I also wish to thank Mr Norman Radcliffe for his advice on timber, Mr A. J. Oliver for checking the proofs, and Mr J. N. Tod for his help in many ways, but mainly for the numerous drawings he did with such care. Lastly I must express my gratitude to the long-suffering staff of Methuen's, particularly to Mr Anthony Forster without whose help this book would never have been published.

Cobham, Surrey   G. K. G. B.
September 1957

CONTENTS

LIST OF PLATES

INTRODUCTION

'Do it yourself' is the fashionable cry today. Every month brings new suggestions of how we can save money and amuse ourselves about the house with a hammer and screwdriver; but I am afraid that many enthusiasts are carried away by the advertisements and end up with no more than a battered kitchen table.

Most prospective boat-builders have some idea of how to set about their task of construction; but, however advanced their manual and technical skill may be, they are bound to run into some difficulties. It has been my aim in writing this book to help the beginner and set him on the right road. I start with advice on choosing the design and carry on to the completion of the job.

The most suitable boats for the amateur to build are the wide range of hard-chine and double chine-built craft of timber construction, which have been developed since the last war. Designers, builders and chandlers throughout the country have brought the building and sailing of small boats within the reach of thousands by new techniques. With one or two exceptions I have confined my remarks to hard-chine and double-chine boats of marine-ply construction.

You may well ask yourself at this stage – 'Have I the necessary skill to build my own boat?' The answer is that an amateur can build a successful boat, either from drawings or from kits of prepared parts, with no previous experience beyond an elementary knowledge of carpentry. The most important requirement is common sense, followed closely by ability to handle the tools required and a determination to carry the job through to the end. You will derive much satisfaction from the results of your labours.

11

I

METHODS OF BUILDING

Before embarking on a discussion of the alternative ways of building your boat, it will be helpful to explain the terms 'hard chine' 'double chine' and 'clinker ply', and show how they differ from 'clinker' construction. Fig. 1 illustrates the characteristics of these four types.

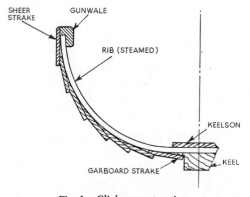

Fig. 1a. Clinker construction.

It is important to explain in detail the difference between clinker and clinker-ply construction as referred to in this book. Generally speaking, clinker construction is not suitable for the average amateur. Clinker-built boats have of course been built very successfully by many so-called amateurs, but only by those with considerable experience, and they should definitely not be attempted by the beginner. Briefly, clinker construction relies on planks overlapping each other (see Fig. 1a). These planks are either nailed to ribs or glued together; they are not of uniform shape and need very careful shaping.

Clinker-ply construction as shown in Fig. 1b has as far as I know no universal name, and it is most important not to be put off because of the word 'clinker'. Sometimes this term is used to denote clinker-built boats using planks cut from ply; this is in fact becoming increasingly popular with many professional builders.

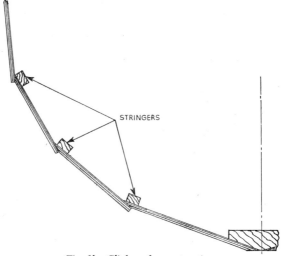

Fig. 1b. Clinker-ply construction.

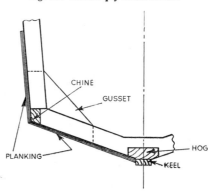

Fig. 1c. Hard-chine construction.

2. 'Yachting World' Utility Pram

3. Sapling Collapsible Pram, folded for carrying

4. Sapling Collapsible Pram, afloat

5. Raven Pram, under construction

6. Raven Pram, afloat

7. Feather Pram

All references to clinker-ply construction in this book relate to the recently developed method, in which the ply panels are glued and screwed to frames as in a hard-chine or chine boat, and to stringers as well. There are more panels; besides the usual top and bottom panel there are two or three intermediate panels, which are joined together lengthwise, as shown in Fig. 1b, on a stringer. The full details of this construction are covered in detail in the chapters on constructing the boat. This method is certainly within

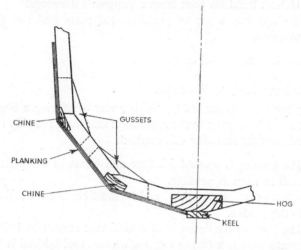

Fig. 1d. Double-chine construction.

the capabilities of the average home boat-builder; in fact, both the boats described in this book in which this method is used are available in kit form only.

The double chine comes nearer to the perfect hull formation than hard chine and it is easier to build. In building a hard-chine boat one is faced with the formidable task of twisting the bottom planks through nearly 90°. As you can see from Fig. 1c, the bottom plank is almost horizontal. For the forward quarter of its length it has to be twisted to the vertical plane where the forward edge is fastened to the stem. The shorter the boat the more troublesome this twist becomes.

The Cadet, the Graduate, and the 'Yachting World' Utility Pram avoid a lot of difficulty by having a transom bow. The whole question will be discussed more fully later, but it is as well to bear these fundamental questions in mind before considering building methods. The home boat-builder can set about his task in three different ways:

(a) He can complete a partially built hull supplied by a manufacturer.

(b) He can build his boat from a designer's drawings.

(c) He can buy a kit of prefabricated parts and put them together.

I shall now discuss these three alternatives.

Completing a Partially Built Hull

To my mind this is the least satisfying way of making a boat at home; and I have come to the conclusion that there are only three valid reasons for choosing this method.

1. The builder is pressed for time and wants to complete the craft as soon as possible.

2. Space at home is limited, and he must confine his activities to the garden.

3. The boat of his desire is of a kind that cannot be built by amateurs, e.g. a Flying Fifteen, whose moulded hull is built of layers of veneer or marine ply.

Some people may be tempted to think that completing a partially built hull is an easy way out and that they will save themselves money that way or cover up their shortcomings as craftsmen. I doubt myself whether, even in the most favourable circumstances, they will save themselves as much as £25 by completing a partially built hull rather than buying a complete £150 boat, and I would warn them that they can spoil a boat just as easily in finishing off a hull as building it from scratch. The decking, thwarts, coaming, etc., are all going to show just as much as the hull itself. A bad joint in the decking looks terrible: it will show through the varnish and be there for all to see.

Building from Drawings

This is the most rewarding way of building a boat, but it demands a great deal of effort and trouble.

Much preparatory work is required and it has to be done with great care. If you build from drawings you make your own frames, which is a boring job. For the 'Yachting World' Utility Pram, for instance, each frame consists of five pieces of wood. Each piece needs a lot of shaping to take gunwales, chines, hog, and floorboards. The same applies to the transom. There is nothing insuperably difficult about these jobs; they only demand common sense; but there is always the powerful temptation to rush on to the more interesting stage. An error in the preliminary work, e.g. in the shaping of the transom, can lead to trouble later on.

Again a warning about cost. The saving in building from drawings over buying a kit is nil. As a small purchaser of timber you will have to pay retail prices. A manufacturer of kits, besides getting his material at trade prices, will waste far less wood.

Building from Kits

This method will suit 80 per cent of home boat-builders as it relieves them of the trouble of marking out the timber. British manufacturers nowadays provide kits of prefabricated parts of many kinds of boat, and they are exported all over the world.

You should read the instructions carefully as the specifications vary in detail. I like the ones that supply and number every item separately; these give you a chance of making variations in the fittings.

You will meet with every assistance from the kit suppliers. If you get into a muddle write to the manufacturer or ring him up. He will do his best to put you right again.

WHERE TO BUILD

I propose to deal with this crucial question under three headings:

1. Building in the house.
2. Building in the garage.
3. Building in the open.

If you ask me how much working space is required I can give you a straight answer – the more, the better. I have always found that I could do with more than I have; but it is surprising what one can achieve in a limited space.

The first boat I built was a 'Yachting World' Utility Pram, and I did the entire job in my workshop on a floor space of 11 × 6 ft; the boat was 7 ft 9 in × 4 ft. I was cramped, but I had a 9-ft ceiling, so I could turn the longest lengths of timber end-wise. I also put the whole structure on trestles so that I could shift it from one side of the room to the other.

Building in the House

Indoors is without doubt the best place for building a boat. For one thing it encourages work. Most builders, like myself, will have to do their work in the evenings and at week-ends. Those odd moments you snatch just to fair-off the last frame would be lost if the construction were carried on outside; and those odd moments count for a lot.

For one boat I built I was in luck. It was a joint enterprise with my next-door neighbour. The entire construction of the hull was carried out in his large drawing-room which had french windows. This showed great self-sacrifice on the part of himself and his wife; and we were still on speaking terms at the end of the job.

There are three further advantages in building your boat in the house.

1. The resin glues you will use all have a rate of hardening directly related to temperature. If the temperature is consistently warm, the glue will set faster.
2. In the house or in a dry garage you do not have to bother about leaving your tools about. In the garden they will rust overnight with the dew.
3. You can probably screw the frames to the floor.

Building in the Garage

The main snag here is that nearly all garages have concrete floors; and this is a serious disadvantage.

Fig. 2 shows a method of securing a wooden plank to a concrete floor to give maximum stability. You can also use Rawlplugs and ordinary wood screws, but the method shown is much stronger.

Some of the small boats such as the 'Yachting World' Utility Pram and the Aquabat can be constructed either on their own packing-cases or on good stout planks resting on, or preferably screwed to, trestles; but the larger boats raise a different problem.

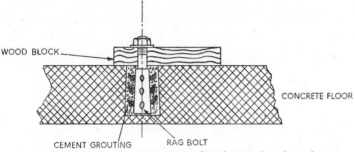

Fig. 2. Wood blocks bolted to concrete floor for attaching frame legs.

The main lines of stress of the frame-keel-stern assembly must be borne in mind (see Fig. 3). The keel and hog in most boats are exerting a downward thrust in the centre and an upward thrust at the stem and transom.

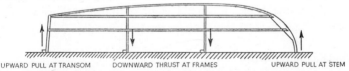

UPWARD PULL AT TRANSOM   DOWNWARD THRUST AT FRAMES   UPWARD PULL AT STEM

Fig. 3. Sketch to show forces acting on floor or building frame due to bending of keel.

Some means must therefore be devised to anchor the frames, stem, and transom to the concrete floor. The two simplest ways of laying a wooden foundation are as follows:

1. Two long solid planks with a cross member at each end to secure the transom and stem. The legs of the frames can be screwed to the planks. Each plank must be wide enough to take all the frames, as the distance from the centre line varies at each station.

2. Two lengths of 4 × 4 in or 3 × 4 in timber can be used with the same timber as cross members. These should be joined as shown in Fig. 4 and screwed together. You can probably screw the legs of the frames to the side of the timbers though this may mean cutting a few slots.

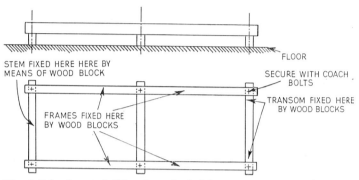

STEM FIXED HERE HERE BY MEANS OF WOOD BLOCK

FLOOR

SECURE WITH COACH BOLTS

TRANSOM FIXED HERE BY WOOD BLOCKS

FRAMES FIXED HERE BY WOOD BLOCKS

Fig. 4. False floor or building frame for building on concrete or in the garden.

As long as the curve of the keel is not very great you can use the second method without bolting to the floor. The lengths of timber are expensive, about 2s a foot for rough-sawn timber, 4 × 4 in. Make sure that it lies flat and is not warped. If you know a builder you will probably pick up an old length of timber of this sort more cheaply than new from a timber merchant.

Building in the Open

You will have all the space you want, but the chief difficulty is the weather.

The ground needs to be as hard and as flat as possible. If you are limited to building on the lawn (which will inevitably suffer), a large tarpaulin will be helpful, large enough to put under the foundations and fold over the boat when it is not being worked on. The tarpaulin will keep the moisture from rising up from the lawn.

If you wish to work through the winter out of doors it will be well worth while for speed and comfort to buy some rough timber to form a frame for a shelter and cover it with a tarpaulin.

The question of foundation has already been discussed. If you are building on a drive with a camber, you will probably have to chock the timber in one or two places to get it level.

Working out of doors is bound to lengthen the job and your labours will probably be confined to the summer months. Keep an eye on your tools. The tools should be well oiled and brought into the house after use. You will also need an extension to the power-point for your electric drill.

The Time Factor

Every time I have started to build a boat, either by myself or with a partner, I have made a resolution to keep a time-sheet recording progress and hours of work; but every time the system has collapsed almost at the outset. However, I am sure that time spent in planning and thinking about the job is never wasted. It is also most important not to over-estimate one's energies; one should limit one's programme to what is possible. Like many other people I do not get home until seven in the evening; and I have never done more than four hours' work in a week in the evenings of Monday to Friday. At the week-end I often manage ten hours or more.

The time it will take you to complete your boat will depend on whether you are building from a kit or straight from drawings. I always use drawings as I enjoy doing all the work myself, sometimes with a partner's help, from the very start. It took me ten weeks to complete a 'Yachting World' Utility Pram from drawings.

Labour

The question 'Can I do it by myself?' often occurs to beginners. The answer is nearly always 'Yes', particularly if you are building from a kit.

At certain stages you must have help of an unskilled kind for lifting the boat and turning it over. Although the hull may weigh only 200 lb or less, it is an unwieldy mass to move in a restricted space and can easily be damaged.

Help can of course be very valuable, especially if you are building from drawings. My last boat was a joint venture. My friend and I were about equal in skill, and by working together we cut down the time of completion by more than 60 per cent. Two minds are better than one for any thinking that has to be done; and when it comes to trimming a ply plank, which entails offering up the plank a number of times and then taking it down again to shave off a little more, the job is greatly simplified if there are two people to handle the material. If you are by yourself, you have to clamp the plank for perhaps only two or three strokes of a spoke-shave.

Screwing up the ply planking is a task for which one can be thankful for help. The setting time of the glue limits the time at your disposal, so it is a good idea to enlist the help of the whole household for various tasks. Small children have a special aptitude for finding vital brass screws dropped in the shavings. I often set my two children, aged four and six, to look for odds and ends that have become embedded in the sawdust.

Beware, however, of offers from well-meaning individuals who say they would like to help you paint or varnish the finished article. That comparatively comfortable task should be the reward of the builder or, at least, the helper who has spent a great deal of time preparing the wood by sanding and filling.

DRAWINGS, COPYRIGHTS, AND SPECIFICATIONS

Drawings

All the boats mentioned in this book except one have been designed by builders or designers of great experience and repute; and appropriate drawings are provided for their construction. It is most important at this stage to distinguish between *assembly* drawings and *construction* drawings.

If you are building your boat from a kit, you will require assembly drawings. These give the minimum of dimensions because so many of the parts are prefabricated and no measurements are needed for their construction. The drawings simply show how the parts are to be fitted together.

Construction drawings are necessary if you are starting from basic materials. They give all the necessary dimensions for building the boat, and they are large-scale, varying from 1 in to the

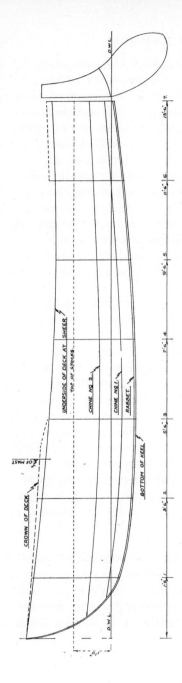

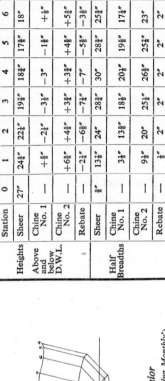

LINES TO OUTSIDE OF PLANKING. OFFSETS IN INCHES									
	Station	0	1	2	3	4	5	6	7
Heights Above and below D.W.L.	Sheer	27"	24¾"	22¼"	19⅞"	18⅜"	17⅝"	18"	19"
	Chine No. 1	—	+⅝"	-2¼"	-3½"	-3"	-1⅝"	+⅛"	+2⅛"
	Chine No. 2	—	+6⅝"	+4⅝"	+3¾"	+3¾"	+4⅝"	+5¼"	+6⅝"
	Rebate	—	-2¼"	-6⅝"	-7½"	-7"	-5⅝"	-3⅜"	-½"
Half Breadths	Sheer	¾"	13⅞"	24"	28¾"	30"	28¾"	25¾"	21"
	Chine No. 1	—	3½"	13⅞"	18½"	20⅞"	19⅝"	17¼"	14"
	Chine No. 2	—	9½"	20"	25⅛"	26⅝"	25⅞"	23"	18¼"
	Rebate	—	½"	2"	2"	2"	2"	2"	2"

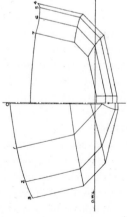

Fig. 5. 'Yachting Monthly' Junior
(Courtesy: 'Yachting Monthly')

foot to 3–4 in to the foot for special items. Full-scale drawings are sometimes provided for the frames or half frames: they make the marking and assembly much easier. It is most important to be absolutely clear about the scales being used. It is possible that on one sheet of drawings two or three different scales are being used.

Some sets of construction drawings give a table of offsets. This is a table of measurements used in conjunction with a profile drawing of the hull (see Fig. 5). There is a base line with the outline of the hull above it. Vertical to the base line are station or frame positions. There are then one or two horizontal lines above these shown as water lines. The table shows the points of intersection of lines drawn from the centre or base line to a water or sheer line. The offset can be of great assistance in checking the positioning of the hull and components. It is not always a necessity in the construction of small boats.

Drawings must be very carefully studied and followed. They are bound to look confusing at first; it is surprising how they sort themselves out after close examination.

Remember that drawings cost money. If you are careless with them, they will soon become unreadable. I always take steps to preserve drawings as soon as I receive them. They are usually sent to you rolled up in a cardboard cylinder, so they are very difficult to hold down and read. They always roll themselves up again and easily get torn. The best plan is to stick them up on the wall of the room you are working in, but that is not always possible. I find it convenient to take two plain building laths and pin my drawing to them, top and bottom. The drawing can then be hung up with a piece of string or laid flat without damage. A more expensive system is to stick the drawing on to a sheet of $\frac{1}{8}$ in hardboard.

Copyrights

When you read a leaflet about a particular boat, you will usually see that a royalty has to be paid by the builder to the designer of the model. Some designs have been published in full in periodicals such as *Light Craft* and the *Yachting World*. If you buy drawings, you generally find that the royalty is included in the purchase price, but not always.

The royalty is a legitimate payment due to the creator of the design for which he holds the copyright. You are bound to pay him for his design, just as you pay an architect for designing a house.

Specifications

The specifications listed in the following chapters are intended simply as guides. I have included a wide selection, covering the majority of small craft that can be built from drawings, from kits or from partly assembled hulls. Most of the hulls are hard chine or double chine, with a few round bilged boats and moulded hulls.

The specifications show the salient points of the boat in question – the outline, the main dimensions, a general description, and some construction details. They are not intended to be instructions from which the boat can be built.

I hope that this information will help the prospective builder to decide which boat he wants to build. At the end of each specification is the address from which the drawings or the kits can be obtained. I have done my best to keep my information up to date and my selection as representative as possible. I do not claim to provide a complete list of *all* drawings and kits available to the aspiring boat-builder.

II

TOOLS

People have often said to me, 'I haven't got enough tools to build a boat.' This is usually untrue. Remarkably few tools are required. Far more important is the ability to use those few tools. The bare essentials can be bought for about £10 but there are some additional ones which make a great difference in the time taken, particularly in the boring jobs such as drilling innumerable holes.

On page 32, I give a list of basic tools. On page 38, I show the additional tools which are a great help. In compiling these tables I assume, of course, that the builder wants to avoid unnecessary expenditure.

I shall now deal with each tool separately, discussing the pros and cons of each type and their uses in boat-building.

Hammers

I am always astounded at the variety of hammers when I see them arranged at the B.I.F. or in a tool-maker's catalogue. For our purposes all that is needed is a hammer which will knock in a nail. If you are using an old one, make sure the head is secure. If you are buying one, buy a good one made by a reputable maker. It is important that the hammer should be the right weight for the user. A hammer which is too light is laborious to use because it takes ages to knock in a nail: on the other hand, if it is too heavy your arm aches and your hammering becomes inaccurate. This is particularly true if the planking is nailed on instead of screwed. A plank can easily take 120 nails which have to be hammered home and clenched over. This means many hundreds of hammer blows in a short time because of the quick-setting glue.

Mallet

A mallet's main use is for driving a chisel: it is also useful for tapping a piece of wood into place. The old-fashioned wooden mallet with a large wooden head is a fine-looking weapon, but I prefer one of rawhide. It consists of the usual handle and a cast-iron or forged head with a deep recess at each end. Into these recesses are fitted cylindrical plugs of rawhide. Replacement plugs of rawhide can be bought, but I find plugs last for years. An alternative to the rawhide mallet is a hard rubber one, in which the whole head is made up of a solid lump of hard rubber. Either of these is better than the large wooden type; and my preference is for the rawhide.

Remember that blows of the mallet will bruise wood, especially marine ply; so if you are embarking on some hard hitting, see that you protect the work with a piece of scrap wood. The bruises on the surface caused by indiscriminate bashing with a mallet have a way of showing up at the last minute when you think the sanding is completed.

Rules

The uses of a rule are self-explanatory. Almost any type will do; if you want to do yourself well, have several. I should warn you that they very easily get lost, and you may find yourself grovelling away priceless minutes in the sawdust looking for one. I have in my collection a rigid 2-ft steel rule which is a great stand-by and gets lost half as many times as a folding or a 1-ft rule.

Chisels

A set of chisels is not necessary in boat-building. You can easily manage with a good $\frac{1}{2}$ or $\frac{3}{4}$ in wide chisel, preferably with a bevelled edge. The main use for this will be to finish off the gunwales and chines and the frames; there are other jobs too where a chisel is most important.

Saws

If you do not possess an electric drill with a saw attachment, you will require at least three types of saw. I will deal with each one separately.

First is the rip-saw or panel-saw, which should be about 30 in long. Panel-saws are the same as rip-saws, except that they have more teeth, giving a finer cut. A saw with six teeth to the inch will be adequate for cutting up sheets of ply.

Second is the tenon-saw. This should be 10–12 in long and is needed for all manner of small sawing.

Lastly, you must have a saw to cut the many odd shapes that will crop up. There are three main sorts – a pad-saw, a coping-saw, and a bow-saw. I recommend a coping-saw. It is a first-class cheap saw, costing 4s to 5s, with spare blades at 2s a packet. It is remarkably efficient at cutting curves through wood up to 1–1½ in thick. The angle of the blade to the frame is infinitely adjustable, and the frame is 4–5 in deep. If the curve to be cut does not allow enough room for the frame to clear the waste wood, a number of saw cuts should be made.

A pad-saw will cut curves without the restriction of a frame, but it is slow cutting as the blade is much softer than a coping-saw blade and needs continual sharpening. When a coping-saw blade becomes too blunt throw it away. It is more likely to break long before it gets blunt.

Plane

The timber for building straight from drawings or supplied in a kit will arrive already planed; so you will not have to cope with large expanses of timber. An ordinary smoothing plane will suffice for planing the edges of sawn timber or for shaping. It can also be used for shaping the profile of the chines, stem, and frames.

Brace and Hand Drill

Apart from the hundreds of holes for screws or nails, a number of large holes will have to be made for various fittings, and these will require a brace and bit. Some of these will be in awkward places, so a ratchet brace is desirable. The cost is about 20s.

As I shall explain later, I believe an electric drill to be the most important piece of equipment of all. But if you must do without one, a hand drill will be necessary. You can get a good one for about 30s.

Bits and Drills

These can only be decided on after careful examination of the drawings and instructions. You will need a set of steel twist drills matched to the sizes of the screws and nails in use, and a variety of centre bits for the larger holes for the fittings. In addition a counter-sink bit is needed. When deciding on the drill sizes for screws, consult the table on page 46.

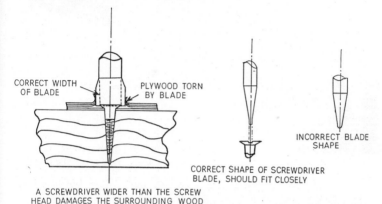

CORRECT WIDTH OF BLADE

PLYWOOD TORN BY BLADE

INCORRECT BLADE SHAPE

CORRECT SHAPE OF SCREWDRIVER BLADE, SHOULD FIT CLOSELY

A SCREWDRIVER WIDER THAN THE SCREW HEAD DAMAGES THE SURROUNDING WOOD

Fig. 6. Correct shape of screwdriver blade and the correct fit in relation to the screw head.

Screwdrivers

A screwdriver must fit the screw to do its job properly. This could lead to a lot of screwdrivers in boat-building. Two important points to remember are:

1. The blade of the screwdriver should not be too slack in the slot at the head of the screw. To be absolutely correct the blade should be a press fit in the slot so that you can pick up a loose screw by putting the blade in the slot.
2. The blade should not protrude past the end of the slot or the screw will cut the wood, as it is driven home (see sketch). Fig. 6.

As for the number of screwdrivers required, you will need one large one with a good long handle to give plenty of leverage with the larger screws. One or two smaller screwdrivers are desirable.

A spiral-ratchet screwdriver will be very handy if your planking is screwed on. When you have to put in a hundred or so screws in half an hour, it is a help to be able to get the screws three-quarters of the way in with a spiral-ratchet screwdriver, and then drive them home with an ordinary rigid-shaft driver.

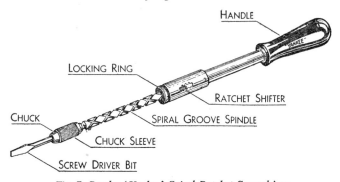

Fig. 7. Stanley 'Yankee' Spiral-Ratchet Screwdriver.

(*Courtesy: Stanley Works (G.B.) Ltd*)

Some people like the ordinary ratchet screwdriver, but I find the slack in the ratchet is often excessive, especially after some use.

Carpenter's Square

Any sort will do, provided the square is accurate. I think that it should not be less than 6 in long.

Clamps

G Clamps are a necessity. However many you have, you need more. Four 4-in is the minimum: six would be better and two 6-in. They must be made of forged or cast steel. The little thin fellows of mild steel strip supplied in fretwork kits, although excellent for fretwork, are useless for boat-building.

Fig. 8. 'G' Clamp.

(*Courtesy: C. & J. Hampton Ltd*)

Clamps at times will have to withstand great strain, so they must be sound and strong. Record and Woden each make a good solid variety, so I suggest your getting four 4-in G clamps, or six for preference. One jaw of the clamp, being part of the main casting, is fixed; the other, on the end of the threaded shaft, is usually fitted on a ball-and-socket joint, allowing self-aligning action.

Accidents can happen with clamps. If the jaws are not gripping properly and are holding in position a piece of wood under stress, e.g. clamping a chine to the frame, the clamp may slowly slip, then

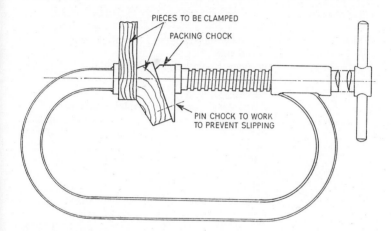

PIECES TO BE CLAMPED

PACKING CHOCK

PIN CHOCK TO WORK
TO PREVENT SLIPPING

Fig. 9. Showing use of packing chock when faces to be clamped are not parallel.

crash about the room like a poltergeist. A 12-in clamp ran amok in my house in the middle of the night and terrified the household. So the surfaces in contact with the jaws of the clamps should be kept parallel. Where this is not possible a small chock can be nailed into position with small panel pins (Fig. 9). I strongly recommend you to have a few lengths of strong cord or string handy. A turn of cord round the clamp secured to a solid fixture is a reliable insurance against accidents.

You will be lucky if you can lay hands on a 10-in or even a 12-in clamp, or better still two or three of them. They come in useful for clamping the chines to the stem. They can sometimes be borrowed from garages.

Carpenter's Vice

Any sort of vice will do; but a carpenter's vice with wood-lined jaws or an all-wood vice will serve best, fitted to a bench; if this is not feasible, a small vice screwed to a trestle will suffice.

TABLE OF BASIC TOOLS
SHOWING TYPES AND ALTERNATIVES

TOOL	VARIETIES	BEST TYPE
Hammer	Infinite variety of types and sizes	8-oz ball pane
Mallet	Wooden, rawhide, hard rubber	Rawhide
Rule	Folding wooden	
	Carpenter's, steel	Steel, preferably 2 ft
Chisels	Large variety	$\frac{1}{2}$ and $\frac{3}{4}$ in bevelled sides
Saws	Panel – rip	Panel or rip medium cut
	Tenon	
	Coping	Coping
	Pad	
	Frame	
Plane	Jack, smoothing	Steel smoothing
Brace	Ratchet and non-ratchet	Ratchet type
Bits	Centre bits, counter-sink	Counter-sink and others according to drill size
Hand drill		Hand drill
Screwdrivers	Simple ridged shaft-ratchet, spiral ratchet, usually supplied with a range of bits	Purely a matter of choice and need
Carpenter's square		A good one that is accurate
G or D clamps	Available up to 12 in	At least four 4-in G or D clamps, and two 6-in forged or two 6-in cast

MISCELLANEOUS BASIC TOOLS

Bradawl, marking gauge, half-round rasp 10 or 12 in, oilstone, putty knife, or any flexible kitchen knife will do.

Cork, sandpaper block, vice, trestles (see text).

Trestles

These are required for two purposes – to rest timber on while you are sawing it, and to support the boat when it is turned over. Unfortunately trestles of differing heights are required for these two operations. However, it is more important to have trestles for sawing on, and these should be about 2 ft high. For holding the boat lower support is required, and it can usually be supplied by two planks with chocks screwed to them and supported on bricks or concrete blocks. The sawing trestle will probably be too high to stand any boat on, except possibly a pram.

So much for the basic tools. I expect some readers will disagree with my collection, but I have deliberately listed only those tools which are essential. There are many others which are a tremendous asset, and these I have listed below. If one has some of these tools one can well do without one or two items in the basic list.

Spoke-shave

To handle a spoke-shave well takes a bit of practice, and that practice is well worth getting. More time is spent in boat-building in shaping and fairing the various frames, chines, keels, and stem pieces than in anything else. These jobs can be done by a good sharp smoothing plane. I like a spoke-shave, and have used one for many years. I prefer a steel one to a wooden one; they are easier to set and nicer to use. The ordinary spoke-shave has a flat surface, but there are also ones with a convex surface. Possibly the craft you decide to build will not have any concave surface to be shaped, but, if it has, a convex spoke-shave is the tool to use.

Surform File

This is a relatively new tool which has been on the market for two or three years. Like many new ideas, it was viewed with a jaundiced eye by some experts. I think it is first-class (see Fig. 10). It is supplied in two forms – either like a conventional file or in the shape of a small plane; in each case the blade is the same. The frame of each is an alloy with a wooden handle. The blades, which are detachable, are made from a strip of high-tensile corrugated steel. At regular intervals over the surface the tops of the corrugations have been ground, leaving a sharp edge. One of the Surform file's great advantages is that it enables you to trim the end grain of a piece of wood without splitting it. It is equally effective on non-ferrous metals. I have found it extremely useful for fairing-off frames and trimming the ply panels.

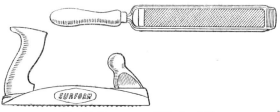

Fig. 10. Two types of 'Surform' file.

(*Courtesy: Simmonds Aerocessories Ltd*)

Screwdriver Bit

A screwdriver bit is an asset on any boat where a number of large screws are required, as a spiral-ratchet screwdriver will not make much impression on screws larger than size 12. In some boats the centre-board case is screwed into position with very large screws. Even if the holes are correctly bored and counter-bored with a drill first, it is a difficult job to get all your screws right home, and a screwdriver bit in your brace is the best way to ensure this. Order the bit to suit the size of the screw. The question of dealing with the large brass screws is discussed more fully in a later chapter dealing with the construction of the boat.

Electric Drill

I did not include the electric drill in the basic tools list, because one can build a boat without one; but I state categorically that nothing would induce me to do so. With its accessories the electric drill is the most useful device I possess and I propose to discuss it at some length.

1. Which Make to Buy

Discussing the relative merits of the products of different manufacturers can lead one into deep waters. The three makes of electric drill designed primarily for the domestic user are Bridges,

Black and Decker, and Wolf. All three are very good value for money. I used a Wolf on my last boat and found it excellent. I own a Black and Decker which has had constant use for six years and has been employed for every imaginable job. Inevitably you meet someone who is vehement in his abuse of one particular make, stating that it is useless compared with another. This is simply not true of the names I have mentioned. What is much more common is misuse on the part of the owner.

There is of course a difference in the accessories. One of the reasons that I chose the Black and Decker was that I wanted a pillar drill stand, and theirs was best suited to my purpose. Each make provides a circular saw attachment. I have a different make of circular saw altogether, marketed under the name of Picador. It does not have the refinement of the others, but is cheaper. Another accessory applicable to boat-building is the sander attachment. There are two types – the disc and the orbital. The disc sander is somewhat limited in its uses as it is unsuitable for sanding large flat surfaces, such as the planking and decking. Its rotary action is liable to mark the wood. The orbital sander is better, but I do not think it is powerful enough to sand the large expanses. A strong arm with a cork block is better and quicker.

2. Looking after Your Drill

People have a strange idea that anything driven by electric power need only be switched on when wanted, used flat out, switched off, then cast aside until wanted again.

First of all see that you order your drill for the right voltage. An electric drill is designed for intermittent use. This is no disadvantage in drilling holes, because between each hole there must be a short pause. If the drill is fitted with a saw or sander attachment, and is continually used loaded to the full, it will soon overheat, and eventually the windings will burn out. It is especially easy to overload the drill when sawing up sheets of ply.

You will see that all drills have small ventilating slots in the body; this is to allow cooling air to pass through it. Inevitably sawdust clogs around these slots; keep them as clear as you can. The gears in the gearbox must be kept greased according to the maker's instructions. Inside the motor casing on the end of the armature nearest the handle is the commutator, which is a small cylinder of copper segments. The segments lie parallel to the shaft. On this run two carbon blocks, known as brushes, in small holders. These carbon brushes wear out. It is most important that they should not be allowed to wear too far; otherwise the copper lead fitted to the top end will cut into the commutator. For efficient running it is important that the surface of the commutator be kept clean and smooth.

It is certain that the lead supplied by the makers will be too short; it is unlikely to be more than 6 ft long. If you are working in the house, you must have a lead long enough to reach any part of the boat. If you are working in the garden or garage a long way from a power-point, your lead will have to be longer still. Then there is a danger of a drop in voltage owing to increased resistance; so you had better take an electrician's or Electricity Authority's advice.

If you do make any alterations to the lead, make certain that it is still properly earthed. They are all supplied with three-core cable incorporating an earth lead.

Finally, be sure to read all instructions carefully. The success you have with your drill depends very largely on how you use it.

3. Application

The main use of a drill is, of course, for drilling the large number of holes required for the assembly of the boat. Always keep your drill bit sharp. Wood takes the edge off a steel twist drill quicker than anything. If you cannot sharpen the edges yourself, get them touched up whenever you feel them getting blunt.

The circular saw is a dangerous weapon, so do not let your mind wander while using it. It is invaluable for sawing up the planking, which is a tiresome job without assistance. The best method is to lay the sheets on two trestles and set the gauge, which adjusts the depth of cut, so that the blade protrudes $\frac{1}{16}$ to $\frac{1}{8}$ in through the wood. On the saw guard is a small mark, which you line up with the line to be cut. Hold the grip on the drill with one hand, and the handle on the saw with the other. Rest the guard firmly on the wood with the blade just clear of it, switch on with the trigger switch, then push the drill firmly and slowly forward.

You will soon get the feel of it. Do not switch on and bring the whole drill down on the wood; it will kick back very hard. The wood must be held firmly or it will slide about. Above all, make sure that the lead is well clear of your line of cutting.

Punches

A centre-punch will prove useful if you need to fit brass banding down the stern and keel, because you must centre-punch the points where the fixing holes are to be made. The drill will not bite unless this is done. It is useless marking the spot with a pencil as the drill will only wander and make the hole in the wrong place.

A nail-punch is most important. I deal with its use fully in the section on nailing planking. It is a help if the punch is ground to the same diameter as the head of the nails to be used.

Rebate Plane

Your need for this plane will depend entirely on which boat you are building. If you build a 'Yachting Monthly' Junior from drawings, you need one to trim the edges of the ply planks when they are being fitted into position. The uses of a rebate plane are discussed fully in the appropriate chapter (see Fig. 11).

Fig. 11.
Bull-nose rebate plane.
(Courtesy: C. & J. Hampton Ltd)

If you are buying a rebate plane, buy the simplest type, i.e. a good serviceable tool without refinements costing about 10s. One can pay up to 35s for the best type with a detachable nose and a very fine adjustment to the blade. This is a specialist tool for the cabinet-maker, and although no tool can be said to be too good, its advantages are not needed in boatbuilding. So I recommend a cheaper type of good manufacture.

Carpenter's Bevel

This is always a help in marking off angles, especially if you are building from drawings; it is adjustable and is used, in the same way as a square, for angles other than right angles.

Gouges

If you are building from drawings and doing the whole job your-self, you will need one or two gouges for hollowing out your boom and Bermudian mast, one $\frac{1}{4}$ in and one 1 in.

SPECIAL TOOLS

These tools are either an asset for building from drawings only or under any circumstance.

TOOL	VARIETY	BEST TYPE
Spoke-shave	Flat face or convex face	Depending on task
Surform file	Plane mounting or file mounting	File mounting
Bits		Screwdriver for hand brace
Electric drills	Wolf, Bridges, Black and Decker	According to purse and taste
Attachments		Circular saw, pillar drill stand and disc sander
Centre-punch		Centre-punch
Nail punch		Nail punch with head ground to suit nails
Rebate plane		Simple type
Carpenter's bevel		Good quality
Gouges		$\frac{1}{4}$ in and 1 in
Ply-marking gauge		

That brings me to the end of the tool list. Remember that tools must be kept sharp. The results you get from them will depend largely on how you treat them.

One last word on cost. When I talk about cheap tools, I do not mean cheap and nasty. Manufacturers of good standing make tools of varying prices. As with so many things in life, it usually pays to buy the best; but one cannot always afford to do so. However, think very hard before you buy the cheapest, which will probably be the worst. A good tool merchant or ironmonger will be glad to advise you.

III

MATERIALS

The materials used in the construction of small boats can be grouped under three headings: *Timber*, *Glue*, and *Fastenings*. Most kits include all the materials required to build the craft. It is valuable, however, to outline the uses and characteristics of the materials in case you take to building from drawings only.

Wood

Except for minor variations, the same types of wood are used for the various parts of all boats and kits. Drawings which cater for construction without a kit always list the wood required, giving sizes and types. There are plenty of timber merchants scattered all over the country: make sure that you choose one that deals in ship-building timber. Some merchants advertise in the yachting journals that they supply all the wood required for a particular boat for a lump sum. It is well worth your while to buy wood in this way; it works out cheaper, and there is a better chance that you will get wood that matches. Matching is particularly important in the case of mahogany, which makes a fine showing when it is varnished.

Methods of timber measurement must be clearly understood. A baulk of timber is sawn up into lengths of 2×2 in section, and will be left rough on all sides to those measurements. When planed the same timber would be reduced to $1\frac{7}{8} \times 1\frac{7}{8}$ in, and it would be known as 2×2 in PAR (planed all round). Make sure that you know what is required and give your supplier the right instructions.

Marine Ply

Although some of these boats have been built of a variety of materials for the hull planking, Marine Ply of Grade W.P.B. to British Standards Specification 1088 is undoubtedly the best, except perhaps for certain tropical areas where there is the hazard of pests attacking the timbers. The Specification calls for a board that will stand a test of 72 hours' immersion in boiling water. The inner and outer veneers must be of the same wood and glued with resorcinol glue. It is also preferable to insist on mahogany ply if buying timber separately. As far as I know mahogany ply to B.S.S. 1088 is supplied in all the kits. All the marine ply manufactured to B.S.S. 1088 is stamped in one corner with the specification number. If this is not stamped on the sheet do not buy it, in spite of verbal assurances. The specification is your guarantee that you are buying the correct ply. (The references to 'ply' in this book are all to 'marine ply'.) It is economical to buy ply in 8 × 4 ft sheets; but if you need small pieces for the rudder blade and centre-board of a particular thickness, buy your ply cut to size.

Marine ply is used principally for:

Hull planking	Transoms
Decking	Rudder blade
Centre-board	

African Mahogany

This is a general-purpose timber and is mainly used for:

Keel	Knees
Hog	Thwarts
Stem	Frames
Deck beams	Centre-board case
Coamings	Rudder

There is no point in discussing the varieties of mahogany. It is not necessary to buy the top quality used for cabinet-making. Be guided by your supplier.

Sitka Spruce or Silver Spruce

It is tough, light, and extremely strong for its weight; and it is available in long lengths which makes it most suitable for:

Masts	Chines
Boom	Carlines
Gunter-yard	Oars
Gunwales	Rubbing strips

Ash

A very strong timber, open-grained and similar to oak in appearance, but lighter in colour. Mainly used for:

Tiller	Boathooks
Wooden cleats	

Canadian Western Red Cedar

Some plans specify this wood for the centre-board case. It is extremely durable, but it is easily split or bruised.

Oak

This will be either Japanese or English oak. Although it is used extensively in building large boats, there are very few uses for it in the types of boat described in this book. In some boats it is used in the stem and for a samson post, when this is fitted.

British Columbian Pine

Sometimes specified for chines and gunwales, though I prefer Sitka spruce for these. Otherwise the main use is for floor-boards.

GLUES

Glue must be used in the building of all the craft mentioned in this book, so it is important to have an understanding of the most suitable types for boat construction and also of the correct method of use.

Of the many kinds of glue available today, only the *synthetic* types are suitable for boat construction. Within this group the most suitable types are urea/formaldehyde and the resorcinol/ formaldehyde resin glues. However, for most of the boats under discussion, whether built from kits or drawings, we need concern ourselves only with the *urea/formaldehyde* resins. These glues can in their turn be divided into two categories, depending on how the hardener, i.e. the solution that makes the resin set, is applied. The hardening agent may be mixed into the resin before use – this is known as the *combined application* method – or the hardener may be applied to one surface of the joint and the resin to another – this is the *separate application* method. The two methods will be dealt with separately.

Combined Application

The urea/formaldehyde resin glues used industrially are usually supplied in liquid form. The hardener must be added to the resin in the correct proportion, and then thoroughly mixed in. However, one firm of glue manufacturers – Leicester, Lovell & Co., of Southampton – has developed a special type of urea resin (in powder form to provide a long storage life) in which the hardening agent is incorporated in the correct proportion during manufacture. The product is marketed under the name of *Cascamite* '*One Shot*', and merely requires mixing with cold water (one operation, hence 'One Shot'); it is then ready for use. By eliminating the hardener stage, the gluing operation is made very simple.

As always with synthetic resins, temperature is an important factor in the use of Cascamite 'One Shot'. It affects both the usable life of the glue mix and the time that the joints must remain under pressure. Below are shown the relevant figures at various temperatures and information on mixing procedure. Full instructions are always supplied with each tin of glue.

Mixing

1. By Weight

Add 2 parts of Cascamite 'One Shot' powder to 1 part of cold water.

2. *By Measure*

Add 3½ measures of Cascamite 'One Shot' powder to 1 measure of cold water.

Put one half of the water in a convenient container, not made of metal. I always use a small jam jar. Add the Cascamite 'One Shot' powder to the water, stirring until it is dissolved. Add the remainder of the water, stirring all the time until the mixture is complete. The glue is now ready for use.

Usable Life of the Mix

9 hours at 50° F.	1–1½ hours at 70° F.
3 hours at 60° F.	40 minutes at 80° F.

This limited usable life is not such a snag as may at first appear. In building any boat you will need to mix a lot of glue. You soon become proficient at mixing the exact amount required.

Pressure Time

18 hours at 50° F.	2½–3 hours at 70° F.
5–6 hours at 60° F.	1½ hours at 80° F.

You will now appreciate my comments on building your boat in a cold garage or in the open air. At temperatures below 50° F. 2 or 3 days may have to elapse before the glue sets. Electric fires or oil heaters may be necessary while the glue is setting; but for the glue spreading and assembling a low temperature is an advantage.

Separate Application

Of the resins supplied with the hardener in a separate container, the most practical for the boats we are concerned with is *Aerolite 300*. It is manufactured by Aero Research.

Aerolite 300 is in the urea/formaldehyde thermosetting group, and with the special G.B. hardeners has excellent gap-filling properties. This is very important in constructional joints. Aerolite 300 is the liquid form of Aerolite 306 powder. The mixture is as follows:

Aerolite 306	100 parts by weight
Water	45 parts by weight.

The exact proportions are not, however, of critical importance. The powder should be placed in a dry jar and the water gradually added to it. Stir the mixture thoroughly to ensure a smooth solution, and keep it overnight to allow all the air bubbles to escape. It can be stored several weeks without damage, and the Aerolite 306 powder will keep for at least two years in its original container with the top securely fastened.

The hardeners are supplied coloured or colourless. The colours are a visual means of knowing which speed of setting can be expected, and they confirm that the hardener has been supplied. For our purposes the clear hardeners are all that are required. The range is:

> Hardener GBQ.X (fast setting, 5 minutes)
> Hardener GBP.X (medium setting, 10 minutes)
> Hardener GBM.X (slow setting, 20 minutes).

The number of minutes shown is the time allowed for positioning components before the joint must be clamped. 'GBM' is the grade to use for amateur boat-building and is supplied with most kits.

Clamping Times

Temperature	10°C.	16°C.	21°C.	27°C.	32°C.
	50°F.	60°F.	70°F.	80°F.	90°F.
Hardener GBQ.X	5–6 hrs.	2½ hrs.	1¾ hrs.	1¼ hrs.	1 hr.
Hardener GBP.X	6–7 hrs.	3 hrs.	2 hrs.	1¼ hrs.	1 hr.
Hardener GBM.X	10–12 hrs.	5 hrs.	3½ hrs.	2½ hrs.	2 hrs.

These times should be doubled when the joint is to be subjected to great stress immediately after removal of the clamps.

FASTENINGS

The principal fastenings used in these boats under construction are *copper boat nails* and *brass screws*. The main function of the fastenings is to hold the wood together until the glue has set. Kits supply screws for all fastenings except for the decking and for joining the ply-planking, but some designs allow for nails to be used for all planking. It is much easier to make a good job of screwing than nailing. I prefer to see screws rather than rows of clenched nails which often spoil the look of well-varnished woodwork. It is difficult to clench nails single-handed as it is often impossible to hold an iron at the point while hammering the nail home; but screws can be easily put in place without help.

Screws

The most suitable screws for our type of boat-building are brass screws. They have proved perfectly satisfactory in thousands of small boats since the war. There is a school of thought that states that only gunmetal or stainless-steel screws will withstand the corrosion sufficiently; they are undoubtedly better, but are far more expensive and difficult to obtain. The fact remains that designers, kit suppliers and builders recommend and supply brass screws.

Screws must be treated with reasonable care and must not be damaged. A screwdriver with too small a blade will burr the head of the screw and probably break it. The object of a screw is to hold pieces of wood together tightly, the thread of the screw holding the wood tight against the head of the screw. It is most important therefore that the screw head should be properly seated in the wood. This will be ensured by a counter-sink bit used with a drill, which opens the hole to the correct size to take the head of the screw. The wood must then be bored to the depth of the smooth shank of the screw to a clearance fit; then the counter-bore must be bored to a smaller size for the thread to cut in and maintain a firm hold. This is demonstrated in Figs. 38a and b, which shows proportionally how deep the counter-bore should be; it must not be drilled to the full length of the screw. If the bore and counter-bore are too large, the screw will not hold. If by mistake you do drill the hole too large, you can usually plug it with a suitable piece of wood or glue, and then put the screw in. It is equally bad to underdrill the holes. The screws will then be too tight and you will risk the danger of breaking the screw in the hole. If you do break the screw in the hole, and cannot extract what is left with a pair of pliers, it is best to drill a new hole.

You should use a lubricant such as grease when driving in a screw. Even so, you will find the larger sizes of screw pretty stiff. If any job requires that a component be screwed into place, then removed again for alteration perhaps more than once, it is a good idea to use a steel screw of one size smaller first, and then use the brass screw for the final fitting. I always keep a selection of steel screws handy for that purpose.

Copper Nails

Copper boat nails are made square in section and should have counter-sunk heads. As copper is a relatively soft metal, it has to be treated with care; do not hammer at them violently. For securing the decking the nails are driven dead, i.e. they do not protrude through the wood.[1] If they do protrude through the wood, they should stick out between $\frac{1}{4}$ and $\frac{3}{8}$ in and the end should be clenched over. Roves are not used on any of the boats described.

Holes should be bored for all copper boat nails. For very hard wood such as oak the size of the hole should be half the thickness of the nail across the corners. For other woods the hole should be half the thickness of the side of the nail. I prefer to counter-sink the hole very slightly when nailing ply.

The procedure for clenching nails is explained in detail in Chapter X.

TABLE OF BORE AND COUNTER-BORE SIZES
FOR USE WHEN SCREWING INTO HARD WOOD

Screw-gauge	4	5	6	7	8	10	12	14
Bore	$\frac{1}{8}$	$\frac{1}{8}$	$\frac{5}{32}$	$\frac{5}{32}$	$\frac{3}{16}$	$\frac{7}{32}$	$\frac{1}{4}$	$\frac{1}{4}$
Counter-bore	Bradawl		$\frac{1}{16}$	$\frac{1}{16}$	$\frac{3}{32}$	$\frac{1}{8}$	$\frac{1}{8}$	$\frac{5}{32}$

This table is reproduced on the inside of the jacket, it can be torn off and stuck on the workshop wall.

---

[1] Brass nails can be used to secure the deck planking, and in many ways are preferable to copper, which does tend to stain the wood. If brass nails are used they can be punched below the surface and the hole filled with Brummer Green Label waterproof stopping.

IV

DESIGNS

'YACHTING WORLD' UTILITY PRAM

LENGTH OVERALL: 7 ft 9 in   BEAM: 3 ft 11 in

DEPTH OF TRANSOM: 1 ft 3 in   DRAUGHT: 5 in or 1 ft 10 in
                                            with dagger-plate down

WEIGHT: Rowing version 90 lb, sailing version 112 lb

Gunter rig. Mainsail only, 33 sq ft

Hard-chine hull with transom bow

General Description

The 'Yachting World' Utility Pram is a remarkable little craft, very strongly constructed and versatile. This was the first boat that I ever built and she proved a great success; in fact, it was *Bambino* which converted me to home boat-building, and so far I have not been able to stop.

One of the chief merits of the pram is its stability. I often carried four adults with ease, and I was still able to row. I did once carry three adults and two children aboard when under power, using a very ancient 48 c.c. Evinrude outboard. The performance would obviously have been very much better with a $\frac{3}{4}$ h.p. or even $1\frac{1}{2}$ h.p. motor.

The mast and spars all fit in the boat for easy stowage, so the sail area is very limited. She is great fun to sail, in spite of having only 33 sq ft of canvas, and perfectly safe. She is ideally suited for children to play about in and learn the rudiments of sailing.

The 'Yachting World' Pram can be built from drawings or from a kit, either as a rowing- or a sailing-boat.

Design Details

Here the designer has been able to depart from the usual practice. Instead of the ugly box section which one so often sees in prams, and the square transoms which result, a slight curvature has been introduced in the frames, giving a well-shaped rounded bow transom. Three frames are used for the construction, allowing the centre thwart to be removed; I found this necessary when sailing.

The hull is planked in $\frac{3}{16}$ in marine ply throughout. The transoms are ply built on to mahogany frames. The chines, gunwales, and spars are all made from Sitka spruce. The floor-boards are supported on the frames, not on the bottom planking; this gives protection for stowage from bilge-water.

The skeg assists in keeping the boat straight when being rowed or towed. It has a hand-hold for lifting which can also be used for securing the boat either on deck or on the roof of a car.

Construction Details

1. Building from Drawings

I built *Bambino* from drawings and I ran into some difficulty as I did not anticipate the stress imposed by the frames and transoms. The result was that the profile was somewhat flatter than outlined on the drawings. For stocks I used two trestles with a scaffolding plank cut in half, the two halves being screwed across the trestles a foot apart. The planks protruded about 18 in beyond the trestles. Although the planks were $1\frac{1}{2}$ in thick, the thrust on them was enough to bend them over an inch (see Chapter I). So one must make absolutely certain that the stocks are strong enough.

The frames are easily constructed and can be marked off full size from the drawings. They are then set up on the stocks, and the hog and keel are assembled to them with the transoms. The most difficult task is cutting the rebate in the chines to take the chine fillet. As prams tend to get a rough time on beaches and elsewhere, these fillets are most important; they protect the edge of the ply.

8. (left) *Gremlin*

9. (above) *Gremlin under construction*

10. (below) '*Yachting World*' *Cadet*

11. Eleven Plus   *12. Fleetwind*

2. Building from a Kit

Kits are available for both versions of the boat; and there is a conversion kit to change a rowing pram into a sailing pram. The Bell Woodworking Co.'s kit is sent in a crate which can conveniently be used as stocks. The frames and transoms are sent out completely assembled ready to be set up on the packing-case. The keel, hog, chines, and gunwales are all cut to length and bevelled. All the other parts are prefabricated as far as possible and require very little fitting. The ply panels are usually cut out oversize and must be trimmed to fit. All the brass screws and glue are included, together with instructions.

The standard kit allows for ply gunwale trim, but padded canvas fend-offs can be supplied at an extra charge.

Plans are obtainable from the *Yachting World*. Kits are obtainable from: the Bell Woodworking Co., Beta Marine, Slingsby Sailplanes.

THE FEATHER PRAMS

Feather prams are built in four hull sizes:

Length overall	Beam	Depth M.A.	Depth Stowage	Weight
6 ft 6 in	3 ft 9 in	1 ft 4$\frac{1}{2}$ in	1 ft 6 in	68 lb
7 ft 3 in	4 ft 0 in	1 ft 5 in	1 ft 8 in	76 lb
8 ft 6 in	4 ft 3 in	1 ft 6 in	1 ft 10 in	84 lb
10 ft 0 in	4 ft 6 in	1 ft 8 in	2 ft 1 in	100 lb

General Description

There is very little building to be done, as the hulls are supplied complete, with kits of components for finishing the boat. This is due to the nature of the design.

This selection of light-weight prams can offer some handy boats for general use. The two larger versions can carry sails with a sliding Gunter rig which permits the spars to be stowed in the boat. Their stability and good performance make them suitable craft for beginners. All prams can easily be carried by one or two people, or transported on the roof of a small car.

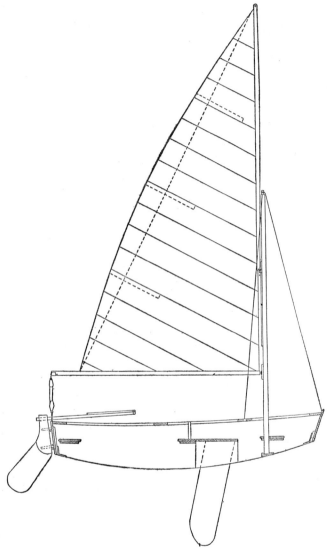

Fig. 12. Feather Pram.
(Sailing Version)

(Courtesy: Small Craft)

Design Details

Feather Prams are frameless boats, the plywood skin being jig-stressed and glued and screwed to the chines, gunwales, hog, and transom. They are all designed on the same pattern and have a transom bow.

Kits are supplied for completing the hulls for the rowing versions. Conversion sets are available for converting the 8 ft 6 in and 10 ft hulls to sailing prams. All the kits include drawings and constructional notes, and they are complete with all fastenings and glue. For the sailing versions the gaff and boom are supplied already glued up.

Designs and kits are available from Small Craft of Southampton.

THE 'LIGHT CRAFT' GREMLIN

DESIGNED BY P. W. BLANDFORD, A.I.N.A.

LENGTH OVERALL: 7 ft   BEAM: 3 ft 4 in

MAXIMUM DEPTH   DRAUGHT: 6 in or 2 ft 4 in
   OF THE HULL: 1 ft 2 in   with dagger-plate down

WEIGHT: Sailing version 50 lb approx.

Gunter rig

General Description

I cannot help thinking that this boat is unfortunately named. She is far from being a 'gremlin' by nature. Provided there is no increase in the costs of boat-building materials before this book is published, you will be able to buy the rowing version for just under £10. This is a triumph of design. Nearly 2,000 have been built.

The Gremlin is designed for the man with the minimum of money to spend and space to build in. She is a hard-chine boat of frameless construction and is capable of carrying three adults under oars or an outboard motor. She can be sailed by two people, but performs best when sailed single-handed.

Design Details

The most interesting feature of the design is the novel method of shaping the bottom from a single sheet of ply. A long V is cut in the ply forward and the sides are pulled in. The three thwarts are permanent fittings, giving added support to the sides.

Construction Details

The Gremlin can be built from a kit of parts or from drawings. She is, I think, the easiest of all boats to build. No stocks are required. The boat can be built anywhere: it can be stood in a corner or moved right out of the way until it is required again.

Designs together with very full instructions are available from *Light Craft*; and you can also find out how to make your own sail.

Kits can be bought from: F. Ryland (Plywood); Chamberlains, Birmingham; Cousland & Browne.

THE RAVEN PRAM

LENGTH OVERALL: 7 ft 7 in   BEAM: 3 ft 10 in
WEIGHT: 56 lb

General Description

The Raven Pram is a neat little craft, cheap and easy to build. It will carry three adults with ease. It is light enough to be carried by one man or two boys. It can be transported on the top of the smallest car or trailed behind a bicycle on a pair of pram wheels.

Construction Details

The Raven is of hard-chine frameless construction and is built upside down, if need be on the kitchen table. The design makes it most suitable for kit construction. The kits supply all timber planed, mitred, and cut to length, with the ply sheets marked out for easy cutting. All fastenings and glue are included; varnish is supplied as an extra. The kit, including one pair of rowlocks and a ring bolt, costs just under £12. It is very good value for money in my opinion.

A novel and very useful idea is that the crate, in which the kit is supplied, if carefully dismantled provides all the wood that is required for the simple jigs needed to assemble the pram. The drawings give full details for construction, including the building of the jigs.

Kits and drawings available from the Raven Boat Co.

THE 'YACHTING WORLD' CADET
SAILING DINGHY

DESIGNED BY JACK HOLT

LENGTH OVERALL: 10 ft 6¾ in   BEAM: 4 ft 1⅜ in
WEIGHT OF BARE HULL: 120 lb   DRAUGHT: 6½ in or 2 ft 6 in
                                          with centre-board down
ALL-UP WEIGHT: 150 lb approx.
Sloop rig mainsail: 42 sq ft
Foresail: 13½ sq ft
Height of mast above the deck: 16 ft

General Description

The Cadet was designed as a class racing-boat for young people and as such it has earned an outstanding reputation since the war. Over 2,000 of these boats have been built in twenty-six countries. It is the small boat in which boys and girls can best learn the rudiments of sailing and racing.

One of the class rules stipulates that neither the crew nor the helmsman may continue to race in the *Yachting World* class if they have reached their eighteenth birthday in the current calendar year. It is a high-class boat with most attractive lines. Space is necessarily limited, but it is an extremely safe boat in every way.

Construction Details

The Cadet has recently been redesigned by Mr Holt so that it can be built as a frameless boat. Kits are available both for frameless construction and for the built-in frame type. Whichever method is adopted, it is one of the easiest boats to build from drawings.

It is built upside down in the usual way with the frame members extended to form the stocks and screwed to the floor.

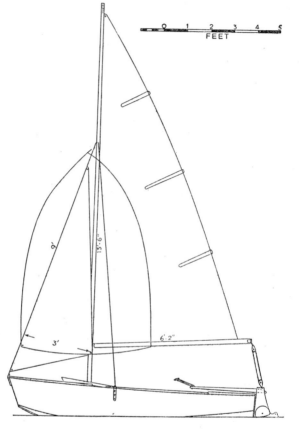

Fig. 13. 'Yachting World' Cadet.
(Courtesy: 'Yachting World')

If you are building from kits, the procedure will obviously vary according to whether you are building from a frameless kit or a kit in which the frames are built into the boat. Both types of kit provide all the wooden parts required, together with the necessary glue, screws, and nails. The wooden parts are planed, bevelled, and bored as far as possible. The fittings can be bought independently or as an additional kit. The mast and boom are supplied already glued up. They only require final finishing.

The instructions show how to set up the frames on the floor. The decking and hull planking is $\frac{3}{16}$ in marine ply throughout.

The sails, including a spinnaker, can be bought as an extra item.

Drawings are available from the *Yachting World*.

Kits with built-in frames can be bought from the Bell Woodworking Co.; frameless kits from Chippendale Boats.

THE 'YACHTING WORLD' HERON (CARTOP) DINGHY

DESIGNED BY JACK HOLT

LENGTH OVERALL: 11 ft 3 in   BEAM: 4 ft 6 in

WEIGHT OF COMPLETE   DRAUGHT: 7 in and 3 ft with
     HULL: 144 lb   centre-board down

Gunter rig with sail area of 70 sq ft

General Description

The Heron or Cartop is the very successful big sister of the Cadet, and was produced to complete the outstanding trio of *Yachting World* boats designed by Jack Holt – the Cadet, the Heron, and G.P.14. The Heron, a hard-chine boat, is one of the most compact family boats available: it will carry two adults and two children for sailing, rowing, or propulsion by a Seagull 40 outboard motor. Herons are particularly suited to those enthusiasts who wish to take their boat about the country without the bother or expense of a trailer. The light weight of the hull allows it to be lifted by two people on to the top of a 10 h.p. car. The Gunter rig allows the masts and spars to be stored inside the boat. Storage in your garage is also simplified, provided you have enough headroom. Two eyebolts can be screwed into the keel so that, with a simple tackle, the boat can be hoisted a few inches off the roof of the car – an ideal arrangement in my opinion.

Remember that any boats larger or heavier than the Heron will have to be transported on a trailer or, at best, can only be carried on the top of a much larger car.

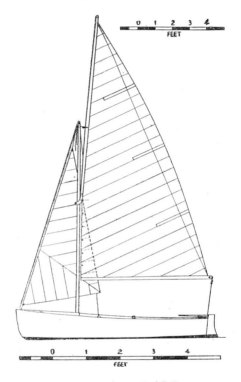

Fig. 14. 'Yachting World' Heron.
(*Courtesy: 'Yachting World'*)

Design Details

The Heron is designed for construction from a kit or from drawings. The number of frames has been kept down to five. Great care in the design has produced a light sturdy boat.

To give the maximum working space there is no aft decking. This leaves a convenient place to stow the outboard motor. The boat is fitted with side benches and two thwarts (these are lacking in many boats that could well do with them). The aft thwart is well forward to prevent people from sitting too far aft. Rubbing strakes are fitted to protect the ply skin, and a skeg ensures steady running.

The centre-board is made of wood, is light and needs no tackle. It is fitted with Kautex pads and rubber stops.

Construction Details

1. From Drawings

The drawings are perfectly adequate for the beginner to build the boat from scratch. It should be built upside down. The frames are extended to form the legs, which, when fixed to the floor, form the stocks. The transom is made of marine ply on a mahogany frame; the skin is of $\frac{3}{16}$ in ply. Owing to the length of the boat, the pieces of ply have to be joined, as the standard sheet is 8 × 4 ft. They are butt joined with jointing strips and fastened by glue and copper nails.

2. From Kits

The Heron is supplied as follows:

(a) Kit of all wooden parts, bevelled and haunched as far as is practical. The transom and frames are assembled ready to set up on the floor to receive the hog, chines, and gunwales. The drawings include details of how the floor should be marked for fixing the blocks and setting up the frames.

Careful thought is needed in planking up the hull. First of all, the bottom planks will have to be twisted as they approach the bow, between the stem and No. 1 frame. This part of the bottom planks should be soaked in water for at least six hours to avoid splitting. The planking is joined on the chine by means of an overlap joint from the transom forward to No. 1 frame, where it changes abruptly to a butt joint. This is all clearly shown on the drawings and is dealt with in detail in a later chapter. A set of all the fastenings, glue, screws, nails, and Prestik tape is available.

(b) The Heron can be obtained as a partly assembled hull. This is planked up with the deck beams fitted ready to receive the king plank, decking, centre-board and case rubbing beads, floor-boards and thwarts, all of which are supple, with rudder parts, fastenings, and spars. The hull is primed with one coat only on the outside.

Drawings are available from the *Yachting World*.

Kits are available from the Bell Woodworking Co., Denton & Partners, Design Boat Co., Scotia Marine, Slingsby Sailplanes, Small Craft.

THE 'LIGHT CRAFT' GRADUATE

DESIGNED BY DICK WYCHE AND DIGBY COPPOCK

LENGTH OVERALL: 12 ft 6 in   LENGTH ON WATER-LINE:

BEAM: 4 ft 6 in   12 ft

WEIGHT: 150 lb   DRAUGHT: 8 in or 4 ft 3 in
with centre-board down

Bermudian rig sail area: 83·5 sq ft or 90 sq ft

General Description

The Graduate has become known in recent years as a thorough-bred light racing craft around the shores of the British Isles. It is suitable for cruising with two adults and two children, and has proved a very good performer on rivers, lakes, and coastal waters.

Weighing only 150 lb, the hull can be carried on the roof of a car or easily trailed. It can be launched by two people off a beach or bank.

A number of clubs have taken up the Graduate as their class boat.

Design Details

The Graduate is a hard-chine boat of the usual ply construction. It has four frames, two of which comprise bulkheads which seal off the fore and aft parts of the boat, making two water-tight compartments with a capacity of 25 cu ft. This gives a degree of buoyancy unequalled in other boats of similar size. The 1,500 lb buoyancy provided will support the boat and three adults when filled with water, which is a remarkable safety factor. Rubber-sealed buoyancy hatches are provided for both buoyancy spaces.

The aft hatch can be removed to take an outboard motor bracket; the transom has been strengthened for this purpose. With the mast removed the Graduate gives a very efficient performance under power.

Construction Details

The Graduate is available in two forms:

(a) Kit of all the timber parts machined and preshaped as far as is possible, requiring only the minimum of fitting and fair-in. The boat is built in the usual manner, upside down. Battens are fitted to the frames to support the structure from the floor. The hull can either be nailed or screwed up with the aid of a resin glue. The only stage of construction likely to cause difficulty is the fitting of the forward bottom planks because of the twist necessary in this type of construction.

(b) Hulls are also supplied ready to be assembled. They comprise a planked-up hull with bow chock and centre-board case fitted. The hull is varnished with one coat inside and one coat of primer outside. The fittings are supplied as a separate item.

Light Craft has produced an excellent little book on the Graduate, giving full information on construction. Drawings are available from *Light Craft*. Kits are available from Small Craft of Southampton.

THE GULL DINGHY

DESIGNED BY IAN PROCTOR

OVERALL LENGTH: 11 ft   BEAM: 4 ft 9 in

DRAUGHT: 8 in or with
    centre-board down 3 ft

WEIGHT: 180 lb   SAIL AREA: 65 sq ft

General Description

The Gull is a new-comer to the fleet of kit-built boats, first making an appearance at the Boat Show in 1957. The Gull is an excellent family dinghy, available as a sailing version, and can be used with a small outboard motor. She is ideal for youngsters to handle, particularly for learning to sail or row.

The mast, being well formed, allows plenty of room to move about. There are alternative rigs – Una with a mainsail only, or Gunter Sloop with mainsail and jib.

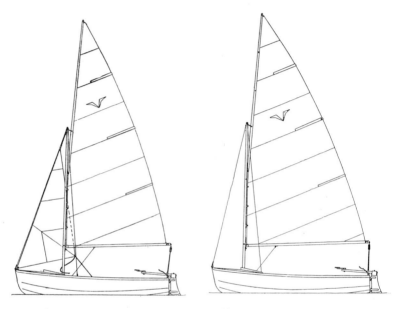

Fig. 15. Gull.

(*Courtesy: Small Craft*)

Design Details

The Gull is a double-chine frameless boat of simple construction. The boat is built upside down in the usual manner; frames for construction are available from the kit supplier. Built-in buoyancy provides added safety and dry stowage for clothing, and saves the added cost of buoyancy bags. The planking of the hull is $\frac{1}{4}$ in. All the wooden parts are prefabricated as far as is practical. The Gull is a good boat for the less experienced amateur to build by virtue of its simplicity.

Drawings and kits are available from Small Craft of Southampton.

SAPLING COLLAPSIBLE PRAM DINGHY

DESIGNED BY GRAHAM BELL

OVERALL LENGTH: 6 ft 9 in   BEAM: 3 ft 7 in

MAXIMUM HEIGHT OF HULL: WEIGHT: 45 lb
    1 ft 2½ in

Folds up to 6 ft 9 in ×1 ft 7 in × 6 in

General Description

The reasons for my developing the Sapling Pram, were that my two children aged six and eight could not row our 'Yachting Monthly' Junior, and that I felt that there was room for a simple collapsible dinghy that could be easily built by an amateur.

The Sapling can be carried single-handed with ease, lifted on to the roof of a car by one person, and assembled ready for launching in two minutes. The load capacity is 450 lb, she is extremely stable – small children can row about in absolute safety, there is no danger whatsoever of the dinghy collapsing while afloat – and she is rigid enough to tow a 14 ft dinghy out to a mooring.

The bottom panels are marine ply to withstand being dragged about on a shingle beach. As an experiment I let in a plate-glass panel 6 × 6 in in the bottom for watching underwater life, and it proved very effective. It was like using goggles without getting wet.

Construction Details

Sapling has a mahogany hog with $\frac{3}{16}$ in ply panels hinged with canvas. The sides are 14-oz canvas glued to the bottom panels and to laminated gunwales; when in the assembled position the gunwales are located in the raised position by a central support, secured by the rowlocks, and the stem and transom at each end.

Evo-Stick Impact adhesive must be used for securing the canvas to wood, and any resin marine glue for gluing wood to wood. The gunwales are laminated from four strips of ply, and are glued and left to dry in the required curve. The total price is between £8 and £9 depending on whether mahogany or some cheaper wood is used for the thwarts and other parts. The pram is not available in kit form at the present time.

Full construction drawings and instructions are available from the author.

ELEVEN PLUS

DESIGNED BY ERIC PARKIN

LENGTH OVERALL: 11 ft
BEAM: 4 ft 7 in
SAIL AREA: 70 sq ft
WEIGHT OF HULL: 140 lb
Bermudian rig

MAST HEIGHT ABOVE THE DECK: 17 ft 9 in
DRAUGHT: 7 in or 3 ft with centre-board down

General Description

At the time of publication the Eleven Plus is the latest small dinghy on the market. It brings in a number of new features to a boat of this size. It is a good beginner's boat. She is normally sailed by a crew of two, but she can easily be sailed single-handed.

She is light enough to carry on the top of a car. Although Bermudian rigged the mast can be supplied extra as a two-piece fitting. This will be a particular asset for those who wish to transport the boat on the car roof.

An alternative forward position for the mast allows for better sailing when the mainsail only is used.

Design Details

The Eleven Plus is a good-looking little boat of double-chine construction. To my knowledge it is the only boat of its size that can be built without stocks of any sort; this in itself is a great advantage to the home builder with restricted space. The manufacturers have achieved a higher degree of accurate prefabrication than usually found in kits of parts. The parts can be assembled on the floor, or on a table: upside down or the right way up, whichever is the most convenient. The hull is built of marine ply, the main components of prime mahogany, the mast and boom of

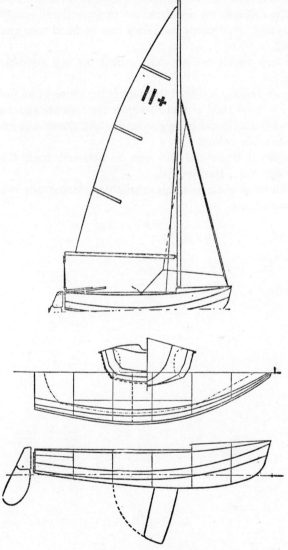

Fig. 16. Eleven Plus.

(Courtesy: 'Yachts & Yachting')

Sitka spruce. The centre-board case is widened to form an additional seat. The rolled-down side decks are preformed and supply built-in buoyancy. Additional buoyancy can be fitted fore and aft if required.

The hull panels are not butt-jointed but are assembled like clinker ply.

The aft decking is dished to simplify the fitting of an outboard motor. A mast jack is used to adjust the shrouds and forestay, which obviates the use of rigging screws and allows adjustment to be made while sailing.

Completed boats and kits can be obtained from Kitboats, Edinburgh Way, Harlow, Essex.

A wide range of extras are also available including sails, rowlocks, boat trailers, etc.

13. 'Yachting World' Heron (Cartop) Dinghy

14. 'Yachting World' 14 ft Sailing Dinghy

15. 'Light Craft' Graduate

16. 'Yachting Monthly' Junior being sailed by the author and his wife

17. 'Yachting Monthly' Junior under construction

DESIGNS (CONTINUED)

FAIREY MARINE FIREFLY

DESIGNED BY UFFA FOX

LENGTH OVERALL: 12 ft   BEAM: 4 ft 7 in

DRAUGHT: 10 in or 4 ft with centre-board down

WEIGHT OF BARE HULL: 160 lb   WEIGHT ALL UP: 250 lb

Bermudian rig

Racing rig mainsail: 63 sq ft   Foresail: 27 sq ft

Reduced rig mainsail: 50 sq ft   Foresail: 21 sq ft

General Description

The Firefly is probably the most famous one-design racing-dinghy in this country. It is built by Fairey Marine by their hot moulded method. Over 1,900 National Fireflies have been built since the war, making these versatile twelve-footers the largest National Class. There are Firefly Associations in North America, Bermuda, and the Middle East as well as in Great Britain. Normally raced by a crew of two, the Firefly has also won great popularity for single-handed sailing. The Single-handed Championship of Great Britain is sailed for annually in Fireflies.

Fairey Marine offer the Firefly as a partially built hull with a kit of prepared components for completion. I have included it in this book because of its great popularity and obvious appeal to the more experienced dinghy-racing enthusiasts. It is a simple craft for home building which will take the average amateur 80–100 hours of work.

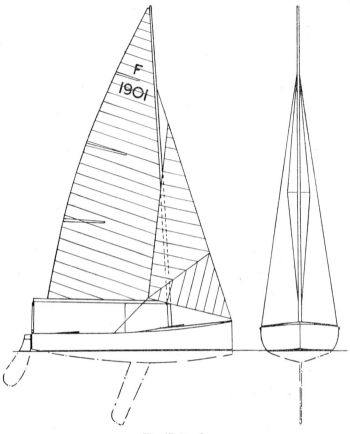

Fig. 17. Firefly.

(*Courtesy: Fairey Marine Ltd*)

Design Details

The hull is $\frac{5}{16}$ in thick and hot moulded of triple-skin resin-bonded mahogany veneers. The mast and boom are supplied in light alloy, sealed to add buoyancy. Even with its racing rig the Firefly has more stability than most 12-ft boats. The built-in buoyancy tanks give a reserve buoyancy of 200 lb. With the bow and stern buoyancy bags fitted the Firefly, if capsized, can be recovered by its crew alone.

Construction Details

Building on from a partially built hull means an appreciable saving in money. The kit includes the moulded hull ready to receive the transom, centre-board case, buoyancy tanks, and deck. These components are complete in themselves and require fitting to the hull. All screws and glue required are supplied and so are all the fittings. The mast, the standing and running rigging, and the boom are ready for fitting to the finished boat.

Hulls and components available from Messrs Fairey Marine.

THE 'NEWS CHRONICLE' ENTERPRISE ONE-DESIGN DINGHY

DESIGNED BY JACK HOLT

LENGTH OVERALL: 13 ft 3 in   BEAM: 5 ft 3 in

DRAUGHT: 7 in or with centre-   WEIGHT OF BARE HULL:
board down 3 ft   199 lb

Bermudian rig

Racing suit of sails: 113 sq ft   Cruising suit of sails: 80 sq ft

General Description

No new boat has ever had such a promising start in life. Within a year of its being designed by Jack Holt and sponsored by the *News Chronicle*, 300 models had been built. It has been adopted by a large number of kit manufacturers as one of their main lines of production. A large number of clubs are adopting the Enterprise as their one-design class.

The Enterprise fills the gap between the very successful Heron and the G.P.14. It is outstanding value for money, providing a light, high-performance racing-craft with a racing suit of sails. It is equally good value as a family boat with a cruising suit of sails. An Enterprise created quite a sensation by crossing the Channel in under three hours, although primarily designed for sailing on inland waters, river estuaries, and coastal waters.

The Enterprise is a one-design class boat and must conform to the Class Association and construction rules for racing purposes. With a total weight of 235 lb she can be trailed and carried with ease. She handles well under power with an outboard $\frac{3}{4}$ h.p. motor, and is light and easy to row.

Design Details

The Enterprise is a double-chine frameless boat of very simple construction. The hull is planked with $\frac{5}{16}$ in marine ply for the bottom planks and $\frac{1}{4}$ in ply for the remainder of the planking and the decking. The design has produced the ideal combination of strength and lightness for kit construction.

The rudder, checks, transom, centre-board, and centre-case are all made from marine ply. The frameless construction gives greater resilience to the hull and lessens the danger of holing the planking if it hits an underwater obstacle.

Construction Details

The Enterprise is one of the simplest boats to build either from drawings or from a kit. It is built upside down on frames which are used as temporary stocks and removed when the boat is planked up and turned over. Temporary building frames are supplied on loan or for a small rental. Most of the kits give very full instructions, and partially built hulls are available from most of the suppliers.

The following firms supply kits and/or partially built hulls: the Bell Woodworking Co., Jack Holt, Scotia Marine, Denton and Partners, F. Ryland (Plywood), Raven Boat Co., Sainter Bros., Wright & Sons, R. Moore & Sons, H. W. Bone & Co., Beta Marine, Bennett Woodworking, Auto-Marine Engineers, Ashworth Kirk, Design Boat Co., DEE-Craft, Kitboats.

THE FLYING FIFTEEN

DESIGNED BY UFFA FOX

LENGTH OVERALL: 20 ft   LENGTH ON WATER-LINE:
BEAM: 5 ft   15 ft
SAILING WEIGHT: 7 cwt   DRAUGHT: 2 ft 6 in
Bermudian rig with mainsail of 103 sq ft
Genoa: 48 sq ft   Spinnaker: 133 sq ft   Jib: 28·7 sq ft

General Description

The Flying Fifteen is fast gaining a fine reputation because of its spectacular performances both as a racer and as a cruiser. It is one of the smallest keel-boats used for high-performance sailing.

Flying Fifteens are ideal for trailing and present no launching difficulties. Without doubt they have the most attractive lines of any craft of this type.

Design Details

Amateurs cannot build Flying Fifteens from drawings; they can only complete partially built hulls. These hulls are made of moulded ply or moulded fibreglass. I would recommend the moulded marine ply. The hulls give a remarkably clean finish with their laminated mahogany keel and stem moulded into the hull. The transom is moulded in with the stern knee. A detachable 400-lb cast-iron keel is fitted.

Hulls are supplied in two forms:

(a) With the keel, stem, etc., moulded in. The purchaser then orders all the components as required; these are finished ready for fitting. The suppliers give a most comprehensive list in great detail. You order the ply for the decking or order the complete moulded deck unit.

(b) As above, but in addition the hull is supplied with the gunwales moulded, the master deck beams fitted, and the special transverse laminated timbers for the keel bolts all moulded in. The breast-hook, quarter knees, transom, set knees, and carlines are all fitted; the other items to be ordered as required.

The mast and boom can be bought hollowed, glued, and shaped.

Moulded hulls and all the fittings are obtainable from the Tormentor Yacht Station.

THE 'YACHTING WORLD' GENERAL PURPOSES FOURTEEN SAILING-DINGHY

DESIGNED BY JACK HOLT

LENGTH OVERALL: 14 ft

BEAM: 5 ft

WEIGHT OF COMPLETED HULL: 285 lb

LENGTH ON WATER-LINE: 13 ft 6 in

DRAUGHT: 7 in or with centre-board down 3 ft

Bermudian rig with mainsail: 72 sq ft

Jib: 30 sq ft

General Description

The G.P.14 is another of the famous trio designed by Mr Jack Holt in the early days of building boats from kits. It has proved most popular; there are well over 2,000 now in use.

The G.P.14 has been adopted by a large number of clubs as their one-design class. This popularity is due mainly, I think, to its remarkable turn of speed for a relatively cheap boat. It has a high performance with a crew of two, but the space to carry four adults with ease for cruising; and there is always room for stowage. Its stability is excellent, and it is suitable for estuary and inland water use, having ample freeboard for this purpose. The G.P.14 is an easy boat to trail and can easily be launched by two people, either from a trailer or a launching trolley. It can be propelled by oars or by an outboard motor.

Design Details

The G.P.14 is a hard-chine boat which is built upside down. The hull incorporates three frames with intermediate stringers between the gunwale and chine and between the chine and keel. The hull planking is $\frac{1}{4}$ in and the decking is the same. Side benches are fitted. The mast is stepped on the hog and secured to the deck beam by means of a mast gate. The centre-board is made from $\frac{1}{2}$ in marine ply and is fitted with friction pads. The drop rudder is also made from $\frac{1}{2}$ in ply.

If you want to use an outboard motor, choose one of $1\frac{1}{2}$ to 4 h.p. rating. Buoyancy bags should be used and are readily available from various suppliers.

Construction Details

The G.P.14 is built upside down, the frames being extended to form the legs for screwing to the floor. The fact that it is a hard-chine boat involves the usual twist of the bottom forward plank and the change of angle of the planking. Otherwise the building is straightforward. It is a good boat for the beginner to build from drawings.

Designs are available from the *Yachting World*.

Kits are available from the Bell Woodworking Co., Jack Holt, Scotia Marine, Fenn & Wood, Small Craft.

OSPREY MARK II

DESIGNED BY IAN PROCTOR

LENGTH OVERALL: 17 ft 6 in

DRAUGHT: 7 in or with centre-board down 4 ft 6 in

WEIGHT OF BARE HULL: 300 lb

LENGTH ON WATER-LINE: 16 ft 7 in

BEAM: 5 ft 10 in

DISPLACEMENT WITH CREW OF TWO: 650 lb

Bermudian rig with mainsail: 100 sq ft

Genoa jib: 50 sq ft   Storm jib: 33 sq ft   Spinnaker: 150 sq ft

General Description

The Osprey Mark II was developed as a direct result of many inquiries for a boat that would be both larger and faster than the existing range of 12 and 14 ft craft, and would at the same time be suitable for kit construction. The Osprey design has achieved notable successes, the chief being to win the 64-mile Coronation Round the Isle of Wight race against 190 competitors.

The Osprey is a one-class design boat. It is a most attractive vessel with sleek lines and particularly versatile; her length reduces her sensitivity to variations in weight. She can be raced with two or three aboard and is safe for family sailing with greater loads. She will lie safely on suitable moorings. She is easily handled out of the water and no more trouble to trail than a 14-footer.

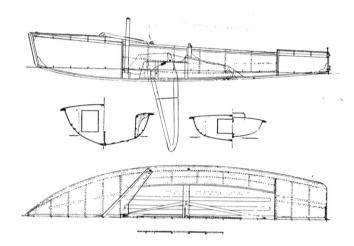

Fig. 18. Osprey Mk II.

(Courtesy: Bell Woodworking Co. Ltd)

Design Details

The Osprey is a round bilged boat built by the relatively new method of clinker ply construction. It is built upside down on temporary frames. Transverse and longitudinal water-tight bulkheads are integrated with the hull structure, giving exceptional strength and considerable buoyancy reserve. The plans are suitable for kit construction only.

Construction Details

Although the Osprey is not the easiest of boats to build, even from a kit, it should be within the capabilities of the average amateur builder.

One kit comprises all the wood, prefabricated as far as possible. Bulkheads, transom, and inner stem are sent out ready assembled for setting up on the floor. A second kit provides all the fastenings and another the paint, varnish, primer, stopping, Cuprinol and thinners for the hull. The last kit covers all the fittings except sails which are supplied separately.

Partially built hulls can be bought with the two main bulkheads fitted, and all the remaining timber parts supplied loose.

Drawings, kits, and partially built hulls are available from the Bell Woodworking Co.

THE 'YACHTING MONTHLY' JUNIOR

DESIGNED BY KENNETH GIBBS

LENGTH OVERALL: 13 ft 6 in   LENGTH ON WATER-LINE:
BEAM: 5 ft   12 ft 5 in
WEIGHT: 250 lb (bare hull)   DRAUGHT: 8 in or with centre-
Bermudian rig or Gunter rig   plate down 3 ft

General Description

This is the boat my friend and I chose for our last building venture. The Junior is not as well known as it should be: it is my firm conviction that it is the best craft of its type. Kits have so far not been produced for it, which is a pity. It is, however, one of the easiest boats to build from drawings only.

Designed primarily as an all-purpose boat of robust construction, the freeboard and the arrangement of her decking and cockpit make her a dry boat, ideal for camping with a tent rigged over the boom. The performance of the Junior is above the standard of the usual knockabout dinghy, but at the same time she has enough stability to make her as safe as one could wish. She has ample seating space: we have been on picnic trips on the Thames with four adults and four children, and still there has been room for the tea. For this kind of joy-riding any good $1\frac{1}{2}$–$2\frac{1}{2}$ h.p. outboard motor will be strong enough. For coastal work I have found that one needs a size larger.

The Gunter rig is particularly useful if you are confined to the river, as we are. The yard is designed to fit snugly against the mast with virtually no loss of efficiency. The mast is stepped on deck and can, if necessary, be taken down while one remains in the boat – this can be a great help on the river. The masts and spars all stow within the boat.

Design Details

The Junior is constructed of marine ply on mahogany frames. It has the advantage of having a double-chine hull, which avoids the difficulty one encounters with hard-chine construction. The hull planking is specified in the drawings as $\frac{5}{16}$ in ply: this can, I believe, be reduced to $\frac{1}{4}$ in without disadvantage. There is a world of difference between bending $\frac{1}{4}$ and $\frac{5}{16}$ in ply.

The frame construction is very simple, each consisting of three pieces of mahogany and two ply gussets. The centre frame incorporates the bench supports. Details are given in the drawings for screws and nails to be used as fastenings. The drawings also include particulars for making some of the metal fittings. This certainly requires some knowledge of metal work if you want to make a decent job of it. If you feel your skill is inadequate, nearly all these fittings can be replaced with standard fittings which can be bought from a chandler. Many G.P.14 fittings can be used.

Although the Junior is not difficult to build, I strongly urge you to get one other person to help you with the work. Many of the tasks can easily be undertaken single-handed, but a lot of strength is required in fastening many of the timbers. For example, the keel and hog are glued up together flat before being secured to the frames and transom.

One last point about weight. Although the bare hull only weighs 250 lb the centre-plate, being of mild steel, weighs 45 lb, and the rudder has a mild steel or alloy drop blade. The total weight, including mast and spars, is just over 350 lb. So, except under ideal conditions, she cannot be launched single-handed.

Designs are available from the Editor, *Yachting Monthly*, 3 Clements Inn, London, W.C.2. No kits are available.

Construction Details

The stocks that Mr Gibbs advocates for the Junior are very much more robust than the ones usually encountered in building

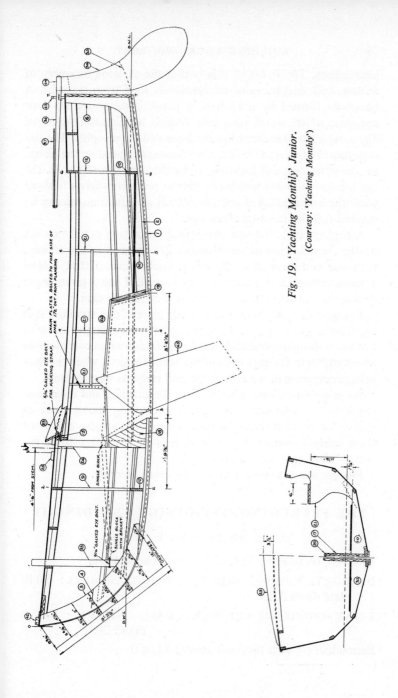

Fig. 19. 'Yachting Monthly' Junior.

(Courtesy: 'Yachting Monthly')

instructions. The result of this is that the skeleton assembly of frames, keel, and transom are absolutely rigid from the start. A backbone formed by a 13 ft 6 in plank is supported on four uprights, which are in turn held vertical by diagonal supports. These supports are screwed to the floor and the uprights. The top edge must be true and planed. The frames are placed on the plank, to which the stem and transom are fixed by small coach bolts. Do not use screws as you will not be able to get a screwdriver to them when the hull is planked up. The frames and the transom can be marked full size from the drawings.

A coping-saw is the best cheap tool for cutting out the curves on the frames. Legs of scrap timber are screwed to the frames, with one end screwed to the floor. Each frame is then braced against vertical and horizontal movement. I have given more details than usual for these stocks as they require care.

The stem is a very simple but sturdy piece of construction. It is cut from a piece of $\frac{3}{4} \times 12$ in mahogany, then laminated with $\frac{3}{8}$ in ply. Fitting the keel and stem to the frames takes considerable effort, owing to the curvature of the keel. However, when that has been accomplished, the rest of the hull presents no problems.

We encountered one difficulty with the coaming and the coaming beams on the forward deck. The drawing shows these as slightly curved, but we found this impossible to achieve and fitted them straight instead. I also think it is an advantage to fit the centre-board case with Prestik tape.

Designs are available from the *Yachting Monthly*.

THE FLEETWIND ONE-DESIGN 12-ft DINGHY

DESIGNED BY ALAN ECKFORD

LENGTH OVERALL: 12 ft $1\frac{1}{2}$ in BEAM: 4 ft 6 in

DRAUGHT: 8 in with dagger-plate down 3 ft WEIGHT OF HULL: 140 lb

TOTAL WEIGHT ALL UP: 167 lb MAST HEIGHT ABOVE DECK: 20 ft

Bermudian rig with total sail area of 84 sq ft

General Description

The Fleetwind is an admirable light craft for family sailing or racing. It is large enough for a crew of two to race. Two adults and two children can cruise in it in estuaries and inland waters with complete safety. In the last three years more than twenty clubs have taken up the Fleetwinds, which is a fine tribute to their quality. The Fleetwind is ideally suited for home construction from a kit.

Design Details

The Fleetwind is a hard-chine boat of frameless construction, the hull being planked in $\frac{1}{4}$ in marine ply. The frames for building can be hired from the supplier. The chines, gunwales, and hog are made from mahogany; the keel and tiller are oak. The mast is of hollow construction in silver spruce.

Construction Details

Over 300 Fleetwinds have been built from kits by amateurs with little or no previous experience. They can also be built from drawings only.

The basic hull kit provides all the timber and resin-bonded ply for the hull, rudder, dagger-plate, together with resin glue, brass screws, and copper nails. There is another kit for the mast and a third for the boom. Both these items can be bought finished from the supplier, if required. In kit form the timber is hollowed out and grooved for the sail with all the necessary fittings included.

The hull can also be bought in part-built form with all the materials to complete it. There is yet another kit for the standard buoyancy scheme, including ply, stringers, screws, and nails. The remainder of the fittings and sails are obtainable as separate items.

Drawings and kits are obtainable from Alan Eckford.

DESIGNS (CONTINUED)

THE 'YACHTING WORLD' 13-ft OUTBOARD RUNABOUT

DESIGNED BY D. W. POLLOCK

LENGTH OVERALL: 13 ft 2 in   BEAM: 4 ft 10 in

DEPTH OF HULL: 2 ft 4 in   WEIGHT without motor: 275 lb

DRAUGHT: $4\frac{1}{2}$ in

General Description

I think I am right in saying that the 'Yachting World' Outboard Runabout was the first boat of this calibre to be designed for home construction in kit form. It can also be built from drawings only. She has smart lines and is safe and stable. Although originally designed for outboard propulsion, a kit is supplied to build a model that accommodates an inboard motor. She will seat four adults.

The hull is hard chine and the transom can be cut to suit whatever outboard is chosen. There are two cockpits, each seating two people. The steering gear is wheel-controlled from the fore and aft cockpit.

A 4 h.p. outboard is the most suitable engine to use, but a less powerful engine can be used in sheltered waters, giving of course a much reduced performance.

Construction and Design Details

The hull is built on frames which have extended legs to obviate the need of stocks. The hull planking is $\frac{1}{4}$ in marine ply for the side and bottom panels; the deck is $\frac{3}{16}$ in ply. In kit form the frames, transom, and stem are sent out already assembled, so that they can be set up at once.

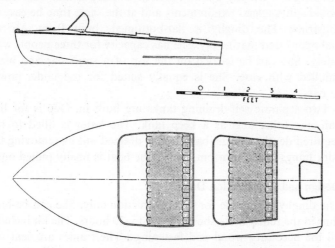

Fig. 20. 'Yachting World' 13 ft Runabout

(*Courtesy: 'Yachting World'*)

The kits are supplied in different forms:

(*a*) Is the main kit and includes all the wooden parts for the boat, prefabricated as far as possible.

(*b*) Covers all the fastenings that are required to assemble the boat.

(*c*) Includes all the paint, primer, stopping, varnish, and thinners.

(*d*) Includes all the fittings.

Drawings are available from the *Yachting World*. Kits may be purchased from the Bell Woodworking Co. Ltd.

BELL ANGLER'S DINGHY

DESIGNED BY THE BELL WOODWORKING CO. LTD

LENGTH OVERALL: 10 ft 3 in   BEAM: 4 ft 2 in
WEIGHT OF COMPLETED HULL: 102 lb

General Description

The Angler's Dinghy was designed as a light portable boat which would suit anglers' requirements and at the same time be easy to construct. The dinghy is flat-bottomed, built from African mahogany and marine ply. She has capacity for three people with safety. She can be carried on the top of a small car and man-handled with ease. She is equally suited for use under power or oars.

Two separate self-draining tanks are built in. One is for live bait, the other acts as a keep tank. The latter is filled to the required depth with the baler and is drained out by removing the cork bungs in the transom, before the boat is finally pulled out.

Design and Construction Details

The dinghy is suitable for kit construction only. She can be built thus in the remarkably short time of 15–20 hours. The kit includes all the necessary wood and fastenings. The frames are sent out ready for setting up on the floor, and the case in which the parts are supplied is used for building the boat on. No drawings are necessary.

An outboard motor can be fitted to the transom, which is recessed in the centre; the motor is protected by the self-draining tanks. Either of the following outboards are recommended: 1½ h.p. British Anzani Pilot; British Seagull 40 plus.

Kits are available from the Bell Woodworking Co. Ltd.

SPITFIRE CRUISER-RACER

DESIGNED BY ALAN ECKFORD

LENGTH OVERALL: 20 ft   BEAM: 6 ft 6 in
DRAUGHT: 1 ft 6 in or with   ACCOMMODATION: 2–4
  centre-board down 5 ft   berth
WEIGHT ALL UP: 1,512 lb

Bermudian or Wishbone Gaff Sloop rig, mast heights 27 ft and 23 ft respectively. In each case the mainsail area is 120 sq ft

General Description

The Spitfire is the largest sailing-boat described in this book and is the very big sister to the Fleetwind which was also designed by Alan Eckford. It is of hard-chine, frameless construction, suitable for building from a kit or from drawings only.

There are two versions of the Spitfire, each with four full-size berths. They are carefully planned for low-cost amateur construction and light enough to trail with a medium-size car. They have good stability for cruising.

A specially designed trailer is made, which enables the Spitfire to be launched off a hard or slipway. The mast can be stepped single-handed and can be arranged to lower, if desired.

Design Details

The Spitfire Mark I, which is the standard version, is fitted with two berths in the forward cabin. They can be increased in width to the centre-line by extra berth beams laid on cross-beams. The cockpit can be quickly converted into a cabin by sliding back the coach roof and raising the stern hatch on radius arms to fix it to the after end of the coach roof. Special clips hold this in place and a sponge-rubber gasket keeps the joint waterproof. The two berths can be increased in width just as those in the forward cabin. The headroom in the forward cabin is 4 ft 1 in; in the aft cabin 4 ft 6 in.

The Spitfire Mark II has been designed for those who wish to sail farther afield and who like the extra safety of a self-draining cockpit. The two forward berths are the same as in the Mark I, but the raised coach roof is fixed and the cabin is extended aft to a bulkhead with doors above gunwale level and a small hinged hatch.

The floor of the cockpit continues aft to the transom, where scuppers allow any water to drain astern. Stowage lockers or racks can be fitted under the stern decking.

Rig

As already mentioned, two alternative rigs are available. The Wishbone Gaff rig gives the lower mast height of 23 ft – a great asset when trailing. It also reduces the roll when running. One halyard is used, as the light gaff is attached to the sail.

The more orthodox Bermudian rig has the same sail area of 120 sq ft. The mainsail is reefed by rolling the boom; its gooseneck is designed for this purpose. There are two jibs of 60 sq ft and 32 sq ft. A balloon spinnaker is also available.

Ballast and Special Fittings

A centre-board of 1 cwt is fitted and a ballast keel of 3 cwt. Provision is made both in the Mark I and the Mark II for a small stove and sink to be fitted in the lockers near the cabin doorway by means of movable hatches.

Construction Details

The Spitfire is designed for kit construction only and is built upside down on temporary frames or jigs. Wood for building the jigs can be supplied with the kit as an extra, but they are not supplied already built up.

The hull kit consists of all the timber required for the hull berths, cabin top, decking, etc. All the wood is planed to size, and all the screws, glue, and nails are included. The hull can also be supplied partially built as far as the side and the fore decks with the centre-board fitted. The rest of the wood and the fastenings are included in the kit.

There is a separate kit for the mast and another for the boom. Both are supplied glued up, but are left square to be finished off. All the fittings for the hull, mast, and boom are quoted for separately.

The kits are available from Alan Eckford.

THE SEAGULL SLOOP

DESIGNED BY IAN PROCTOR

LENGTH OVERALL: 18 ft 6 in   LENGTH ON WATER-LINE: 17 ft 3 in

BEAM: 6 ft 9 in

DRAUGHT: 1 ft 5 in or 3 ft 8 in   WEIGHT ALL UP: 15 cwt with keel down   approx.

Masthead Sloop rig

Mainsail: 100 sq ft; Jib: 70 sq ft; Genoa: 115 sq ft; Storm jib: 30 sq ft; Spinnaker: 150 sq ft

General Description

The Seagull is one of the latest boats to be produced in kit form. It is one of my favourites, and I hope that she will be the next boat that I build.

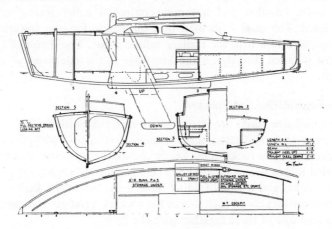

Fig. 21. Seagull sloop.
(*Courtesy: Bell Woodworking Co. Ltd*)

Designed for coastal, estuary, and inland cruising, this staunch little sloop has been rigorously tested under all conditions. She is shown in plate 21 standing up to a squall of 32 knots under her full working sail. The hull is constructed on the clinker-ply method, giving the advantages of a round bilged boat. Combined with the generous beam and stiff hull, this gives her excellent handling qualities and seaworthiness.

A number of ingenious ideas have been incorporated into the design, of which the retractable keel is the most important. This slides up and down on rollers into a trunk like a dagger-plate on a dinghy, the cast-iron ballast bulb lying nearly flush with the dead-wood beneath the hull when the keel is retracted. The hoisting mechanism ensures that the keel cannot be lost or the hull damaged if it is lowered too soon. This type of keel has a number of advantages. With the keel up the draught of 1 ft 5 in allows cruising in shallow water denied to deeper boats, and a standard lifting rudder can be used. Also the boat can be left at moorings which dry out without harm.

The Masthead rig has been chosen because it allows a variety of sail areas to be used to suit all conditions. The small mainsail is easily handled and a remote-controlled roller reefing gear is fitted. The mast is pivoted in a tabernacle for easy lowering, which is also a help for trailing behind a car. The thrust of the mast is taken directly on the keel case to the backbone of the hull.

Accommodation and Stowage

Two full-size bunks are fitted, one on each side, with sitting head-room over each. There is a small galley to starboard with cooking stove and plate racks; a bucket or chemical closet is to port in a sealed locker with a gasket lid. There is good stowage forward of the bunks, and a small folding table is hinged to the keel case. There are lockers on each side of the cockpit. The outboard motor fits into one of these together with the fuel.

The boom can be raised and secured to the back-stay and used to support a tent cover. With the cabin roof pushed right forward this gives 6 ft 3 in headroom over most of the cabin and cockpit floor. A hatch on the aft deck permits the outboard to be clamped to the transom. A special trailer is available to carry the Seagull, and she can be launched from this.

Design and Construction Details

The Seagull is designed to be built from a kit only. An interesting feature of the design is that the ballast bulb is put at the foot of the keel. This gives far greater stabilizing leverage than the usual method of having the ballast fixed close beneath the hull and a relatively light keel. The lateral resistance of the keel is increased especially when the boat is heeled by the barrier effect of the specially shaped bulb, which prevents 'tip' losses. When a boat heels over, the water tends to be forced down the keel or keel-plate; but the bulb on the end of the keel interrupts the flow of water.

The Seagull is built upside down. The hull incorporates four bulkhead frames; and in addition there are three temporary frames supplied in the kit which are returnable. Apart from the size and the amount of work involved, which is inevitable in a craft of these dimensions, there is nothing particularly difficult in the construction of a Seagull. I think it unwise to try and build her single-handed. The prefabricated parts, which are absolutely first-class, remove most of the anxiety in building this boat.

The kits are briefly as follows:

(a) The kit for the hull and all other wooden parts required to complete the boat. The bulkheads, transom, and inner stem are sent out ready to be set up on the floor. The keel case and rudder stock are already assembled, the mast and boom glued up and the cabin sides profiled ready to take the Perspex windows.

(b) All the fastenings, glue, screws, nails, and Prestik tape.

(c) The fittings and keel with its tackle, together with all the running and standing rigging.

(d) The paints, varnish, primer, stopper, and thinners for painting the hull in two colours and the cabin-top green. The decks and the interior are varnished, except the cabin sides and ply roof, which are painted.

The sails and the trailer are available separately. The drawings and the kits are available from the Bell Woodworking Co.

THE BELL BASIC HULL

DESIGNED BY THE BELL WOODWORKING CO. LTD

The overall length of the hull can vary from 18 to 26 ft. The beam is 6 ft 8 in. Approximate weight of completed 19 ft hull less engine 14 cwt.

General Description

The Bell Basic Hull is without doubt a most ingenious addition to the growing range of boats supplied in kit form. The Bell Woodworking Co. designed it to answer the call from many quarters for a craft in the region of 20 ft. The result is a strongly stressed skin basic hull of proven design, adequate flare, and riding sections, which lends itself to being finished off in the widest range of types and lengths consistent with the chosen beam. The beam in all cases is 6 ft 8 in. Within the range listed below this beam allows for safe

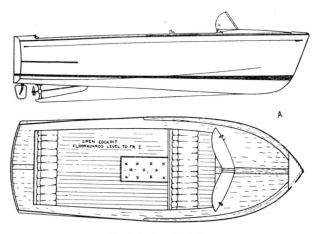

Craft 18 ft to 23 ft long

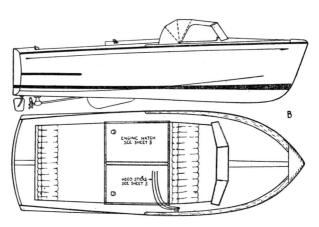

Fast runabout up to 26 ft

Fig. 22. Bell Basic Hull (1).

(*Courtesy: Bell Woodworking Co. Ltd*)

boats for estuary, off-shore and coastal sailing in reasonable weather:

> Fast runabouts up to 26 ft long.
> Medium-powered runabouts up to 23 ft long.
> Day cruisers up to 22 ft long.
> Cabin cruisers up to 21 ft long.

Cabin cruisers can be built up to 26 ft long, provided that the cabin height from the floor is restricted to 4 ft 9 in; even then the boat should be confined to inland waters. All types of marine engine from 8 to 120 h.p. are suitable.

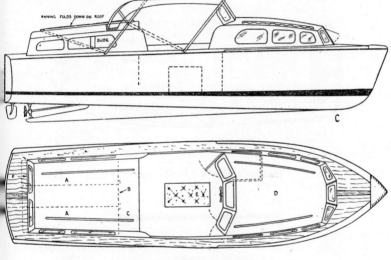

Fig. 23. Bell Basic Hull (2).
River and canal craft up to 26 ft.

(*Courtesy: Bell Woodworking Co. Ltd*)

Design Details

The Basic Hull can only be built from a kit, and the drawings are supplied for that purpose only; so they are only assembly drawings.

Sheet I shows a floor plan of how to set up the frames. I have included a suggested layout for a false floor or foundation for building in the open, as I think it unlikely that many people will be able to build this boat in the house. Sheet I also gives details of various joints for the main hull. Sheet II completes the details of the hull assembly with a few other details. Sheet III covers the fitting of the keel, stern-tube, cabin top, etc. Figs. 22–5 give five suggestions for completing the hull with further alternatives for w.c. and bunk arrangements.

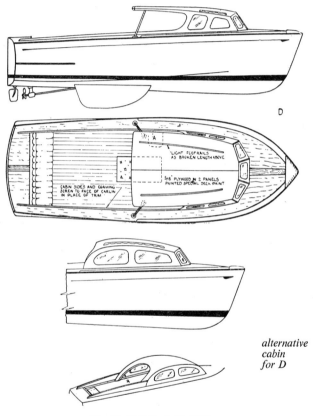

alternative
cabin
for D

Fig. 24. Bell Basic Hull (3).
Craft 18 ft to 22 ft long.
(*Courtesy: Bell Woodworking Co. Ltd*)

The first thing that impressed me when I examined the plans of the Basic Hull was the remarkable simplicity and at the same time the versatility of the design.

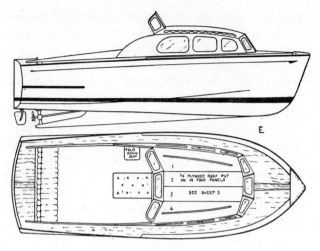

Craft 18 ft to 21 ft long

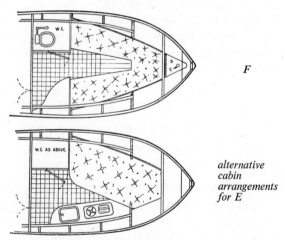

F

*alternative
cabin
arrangements
for E*

Fig. 25. Bell Basic Hull (4)

(Courtesy: Bell Woodworking Co. Ltd)

Construction Details

The hull is assembled upside down in the usual manner, the frames
having horns extended to screw to the floor. The hull planking is
$\frac{3}{8}$ in marine ply with $\frac{5}{16}$ in for the topsides and decking. In the

19-ft hull there are eight frames and two stringers between the keel and the chine; and there are two more between each chine and the gunwale, giving considerable rigidity.

There are two types of keel available – the normal central deadwood keel, or short twin keels, which are a great asset for craft that have to take the ground at moorings.

Anyone contemplating building from the Basic Hull would be well advised to arrange an appointment with the suppliers and visit them, if they are not absolutely clear which type of hull they want or which additional parts they should order for any particular type of hull. The completion of the hull is straightforward, but for the upper work and the fittings the builder is left to himself. This kit is designed for those many people who wish to complete the craft to suit their individual requirements. Over a hundred kits have been sold so far.

The supplier's price-list gives the cost of a 19-ft Basic Hull kit, and the cost of each additional foot required. Cabin front and cabin windshields are also available as separate items. There is also a comprehensive list of other timbers and fittings.

Drawings, kits, and price-lists can be obtained from the Bell Woodworking Co. Ltd.

THE 'YACHTING MONTHLY' SENIOR

DESIGNED BY KENNETH GIBBS

LENGTH OVERALL: 16 ft
BEAM: 6 ft 0½ in
TOTAL WEIGHT, with all gear and crew of two: 1,450 lb
Weight for trailing: 950 lb
Weight less spars, rigging, and gear: 750 lb
Bermudian or Gunter rig

LENGTH ON WATER-LINE: 15 ft 1½ in
DRAUGHT: 10 in or 3 ft with the centre-board down

General Description

The 'Yachting Monthly' Senior is the big sister of the Junior and has proved extremely popular. She is, in fact, a scaled-up version

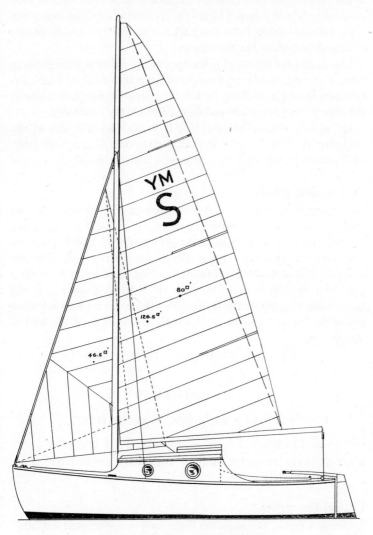

Fig. 26. 'Yachting Monthly' Senior.

(Courtesy: 'Yachting Monthly')

of the Junior with the necessary alterations to provide a cabin with sleeping berths in a larger boat. The method of construction is the same – double chine – and the boat can be planked in marine ply, or aluminium sheet for the tropics.

The Senior is a thoroughly well-proportioned boat with pleasing lines. There is a surprising amount of space in the cabin, which has two berths and a cooking locker. The large sliding hatch allows the crew to sail her while standing comfortably in the dry.

Storage for an outboard motor is available under one of the cockpit seats. The Senior is light enough to be trailed behind a car, or it can be transported by carrier at a reasonable cost.

Construction Details

Unfortunately the Senior cannot be bought in kit form. It can therefore only be built from drawings. This should not deter the enthusiast: space is likely to be the only problem. The boat can be built either upside down on stocks or the right way up. For the amateur upside down is probably the best: it is easier to build a firm base for the boat to be built on than to build a suitable framework to support the frames. For the latter method laths are nailed to the roof rafters to support the frames until the hull is planked up.

Drawings are obtainable from the *Yachting Monthly*.

THE AQUABAT

DESIGNED BY NORMAN RADCLIFFE

OVERALL LENGTH: 7 ft   BEAM: 3 ft 6 in
WEIGHT LESS ENGINE: 70 lb   MAXIMUM DRAUGHT: 8 in
    approximately

General Description

As far as I know, the Aquabat is the only water-scooter available for home construction from a kit of parts. It is constructed from marine ply and mahogany and propelled by an outboard motor mounted in a well in the centre of the hull, with the driver sitting behind it steering by what are in effect handlebars fitted to the motor, the speed being controlled by the normal throttle. Any outboard motor up to $2\frac{1}{2}$ h.p. can be used, and, in the case of British Seagull and Anzani motors, 4 h.p. can be used. The outboard can be easily removed for transporting the hull, which can be carried on the roof of a car.

The Aquabat outboard scooter is designed to give a lot of fun and excitement without the dangers that excessive speeds can bring when such scooters are used on calm waters. It is not a high-speed racing-craft, but a cheap safe craft which can carry two children or one adult at least.

For those who like some excitement the Aquabat can be used as a pair of water skis with the rider sitting or standing. In this way the Aquabat has been towed behind a speedboat at 30 m.p.h. The only modification that is required is an eye-plate for towing under the bow instead of on top of the deck, and of course no outboard is fitted.

Construction Details

The Aquabat is of simple construction with five water-tight compartments, providing considerable built-in buoyancy. Water cannot get into the hull or engine. The cost of the kit is £15 plus the cost of an outboard which many boat owners may have already. Even if you have to buy an outboard the total cost will be little more than half of the cost of the majority of other types of water-scooters on the market.

Kits and drawings are available from Messrs Cousland & Browne Ltd.

THE WAYFARER

DESIGNED BY IAN PROCTOR

LENGTH OVERALL: 16 ft

BEAM: 6 ft $0\frac{1}{2}$ ins

DRAUGHT: 8 in or 3 ft 10 in with centre-board down

WEIGHT OF BARE HULL: 370 lb

Bermudian Rig. Total sail area:
Main and Jib 125 sq ft

Main and Genoa 140 sq ft

General Description

At the time of writing the Wayfarer is not generally available, although on the strength of the success of the prototypes, she has already been adopted by the Watermouth Yacht Club, and a number have been ordered. She was on show at the 1958 National Boat Show.

The Wayfarer has been designed mainly as a camping boat; she is, I believe, the only camping boat of this size available in kit form. A number of novel features have been included in the design to aid the camper. The mast is housed in a tabernacle for easy lowering under the bridges, there is a compartment for stowing an outboard motor, and watertight stowage for clothes and bedding. The flat raised flooring gives ample room for two adults to sleep and the detachable side-benches make an additional bunk for a child. A tent cover can be slung over the boom to cover the cockpit.

The Wayfarer is well suited for trailing behind a car and is equally at home on inland waters or on the coast. She will lie safely on exposed moorings and is robust enough to take the ground on moorings which dry out.

Construction Details

Kits will shortly be available complete with assembly drawings. The boat is built upside down on temporary frames. Being a frameless boat, frames are supplied on loan with the kit. The double-chine hull has attractive lines and simplifies the construction.

The hull is built of marine ply Sitka spruce for the chines and gunwales. African mahogany is used for the remaining timbers.

Kits are available from Small Craft Ltd., West End, Southampton.

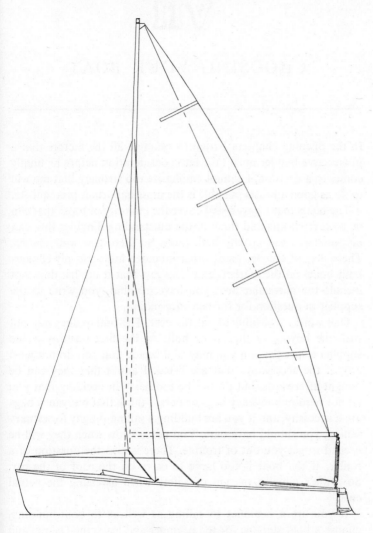

Fig. 27. Wayfarer.

(Courtesy: Small Craft)

VII

CHOOSING YOUR BOAT

In the opening chapters I tried to examine all the factors that a prospective builder must take into consideration before he finally comes to a decision. I cannot emphasize too strongly that the will to do as good a job as possible is the most important prerequisite.

The boats that I have listed cover the majority of those that can be built from kits and three of the outstanding dinghies that can be purchased as partially built hulls. So there is a wide choice. There are, of course, many other moulded hulls and ply clinker-built boats on the market, and I suggest that if my list does not include the particular boat you have in mind, you write to the supplier in question for further information.

One word of warning about the cost. The outlay does not end with the buying of the kit or hull. At the first scrutiny of the supplier's specification you may well decide that you do not need any of the accessories that are listed. I admit that they can be bought afterwards, but do not be too hasty in deciding that you do not require buoyancy bags or oars. I think that buoyancy bags are a necessity; and if you are building a sailing-dinghy for estuary sailing, you should have oars. You never know when they will be needed to get you out of trouble. There is also the question of a trailer, if the boat is too large to carry on the roof of the car. So always allow a margin of safety when assessing the actual cost.

If you are a beginner to sailing as well as to boat-building, choose a boat suitable for the beginner and leave the Osprey and similar craft to the more experienced sailors. The ardour of yourself and your family can so easily be damped by frequent capsizes in the early stages through lack of experience.

18. *Flying Fifteen*

19. *'News Chronicle' Enterprise*
    Sailing Dinghy

20. 'Yachting Monthly' Senior

21. Seagull Sloop

For those who are having a try at both home boat-building and sailing for the first time, and do not want to risk too much money, I strongly recommend one of the excellent sailing-prams. These little craft are being sold in increasing numbers. I started with the 'Yachting World' Utility Sailing Pram for this reason – one can have a great deal of fun with her and learn a lot about sailing. But on the whole the prams are not as simple to build as some of the larger boats. The easiest of all, I think, is the Enterprise.

I have included some partially built hulls for the more experienced sailor who still desires to have a hand in building his own boat. The ones I have mentioned are not suitable for the average amateur to construct. The suppliers of the moulded-hull kits and clinker-built hull kits also supply other craft in a wide range, and further information can be obtained from them.

If you are confined to river sailing and intend to use an outboard motor as well, you will have to moor the boat with the attendant dangers and the risk of her being knocked about. For this type of sailing you will be well served by the 'Yachting Monthly' Junior, which is the most robust of the hard-chine or double-chine boats. As no kits are available, you will have to build from drawings only.

If you wish to sail and race with a club, it is as well to make sure that the boat you choose is raced by your local club. In Appendix A I have listed clubs that sail the class boats mentioned in this book, and the addresses of all Class Association secretaries. I cannot pretend that my list is complete. Each Class Association lays down a set of rules for the racing of the boats in that class and in many cases there is information about the construction of the boat. For instance, there is often information about the tolerances of the critical measurements, i.e. the overall length, beam, sail area, etc.: these may be plus or minus $\frac{1}{8}$ in on the measurements shown on the drawings. Some rules allow a certain latitude which enables the owner to make minor modifications to suit his own taste, but this is not always so.

If you are not building a class boat, you can of course go ahead and do what you like to your boat; but see that any alterations you make are an improvement and not a hindrance to good sailing. It is most unwise to tinker with the design unless you are yourself an expert. Remember that the boat has been designed by an expert for a particular purpose to suit given conditions, and alterations may easily reduce the efficiency rather than improve it. Finally, do not fit endless gadgets; they only clutter up the boat when you want as much room as you can get.

Frequently the owner of a home-built boat begins by saying that he does not intend to race it and proceeds to make a few major modifications. Then he changes his mind and finds to his annoyance that these have to be eliminated if the boat is to be registered in its class.

It is a good idea to insure your completed boat, especially if it is going to be trailed about the country. Any insurance company or agent will give you particulars. The rates are reasonable, involving a higher premium for time afloat and a lower one ashore.

Placing Your Order

Before finally placing your order, make certain that you have all the facts before you. Most suppliers publish their terms of business somewhere on their brochure. Read them carefully, particularly regarding the dispatch of the kit or hull. The same applies if you are ordering the timber from a timber merchant. Damage must usually be reported within three days of receipt. It is often impractical to examine the contents of the kit or each piece of timber on arrival; but it is no good complaining two or three weeks after you have received the goods that a sheet of ply has been badly scratched or that a spike has penetrated the case of your kit and split a vital part. The conditions of transport are based on the statutory regulations governing carriers.

I am fortunate in that the delivery lorry in my area has made a great many journeys to my house at various times with loads of timber, and the driver knows what to do. Being a powerful chap with an amiable disposition he always makes himself helpful. If my wife is out, he unloads and puts the wood in the garage. You must make the necessary arrangements for the receipt of the hull, kit, or timber. Often the drivers are single-handed and cannot be expected to unload a 250-lb hull on their own, quite apart from the risk of damage.

	CON-STRUCTION	AVAILABILITY	REMARKS
'YAC PR	Hard chine	Kits or hulls	Separate kit available to convert rowing to sailing version
FEA¹	Hard chine	Kits or hulls	
	Hard chine	Kits or hulls	
	Hard chine	Kits or hulls	ditto
	Hard chine	Kits or hulls	
	Hard chine	Kits or hulls	ditto
	Hard chine	Kits or hulls	
'LIG	Hard chine	Kits	Can be converted for sail
RAV	Hard chine	Kits	
'YAC	Hard chine	Kits or hulls	
'YAC	Hard chine	Kits or hulls	
'LIG	Hard chine	Kits or hulls	
ELE'	Double chine	Kits or hulls	No stocks required
GUL	Double chine	Kits or hulls	
FIRE	Moulded hull for completion only	Hull	
'NEV EN	Double chine	Kits or hulls	
FLY	Moulded hull	Hulls	
G.P.	Hard chine	Kits or hulls	
OSPI	Clinker ply	Kits or hulls	Assembly drawings only
'YAC	Double chine	No kits	
FLE!	Double chine	Kits or hulls	
13-FI	Hard chine	Kits or hulls	
BEL:	Flattie	Kits or hulls	
SPIT	Double chine	Kits or hulls	Assembly drawings only
SEA	Clinker ply	Kits or hulls	Assembly drawings only
BEL:	Hard chine	Kits or hulls	Assembly drawings only
'YAC	Double chine	Hulls	
AQU		Kits or hulls	
WA\	Double chine	Kits	
SAP!	Flattie		Drawings only

If you order all the timber, your first task is to check it over carefully and mark or number it in some way. If your drawings number each part in sequence for assembly, it is obviously much easier to number the separate pieces accordingly. It is likely that a number of short lengths of one size of timber will be supplied in one long length by the timber merchant; you must cut it up to the right lengths and mark them all.

This advice may seem superfluous, but it is the easiest thing in the world to get the bits mixed up and cut the wrong piece, causing wastage and necessitating a replacement. On our 'Yachting Monthly' Junior our side benches were out of line for that reason. When marking the timber use a soft pencil or chalk and mark lightly. A hard pencil digs in and spoils the surface of the wood.

Store the timber flat, especially the long lengths, with two or three weights such as bricks at the ends and one in the middle. Change in temperature often causes timber to warp. Do not lean chines or keel against a wall; they will certainly warp. Take care of the packing-case or crate in which the kit arrived. It will either be useful in the construction of the boat or it can be returned.

VIII

CONSTRUCTION – STAGE I

I have divided the construction of boats into four stages for the sake of simplicity. The first three stages are subdivided into parts (*a*) and (*b*), the former covering the making of the components required in the latter which deals with the assembly. Part (*a*) is therefore for the person building from drawings only. I have tried to cover all the peculiarities of the boats mentioned in this book, and the various methods of completing each task. There should be little or no difference between assembling the components supplied by manufacturers and assembling those made from drawings. Parts (*a*) and (*b*) will cover hard-chine and double-chine boats only.

Part (*c*) will deal with the procedure for frameless boats where this differs from (*a*) and (*b*). Part (*d*) will cover the different aspects of clinker-ply construction.

I have tried to keep to simple amateur's language and only resort to technical names where this is absolutely necessary.

The construction of these boats follows the same pattern in the main, but there are of course a number of variations according to the boat. I must emphasize again that these construction notes are in no way intended to take the place of drawings or the supplier's instructions sent out with the kit: they are complementary to them.

STAGE I

(*a*) Building Frames and Transom and cutting out the Knees

The *frames* in question are those which are built into the boats and not those which are used as stocks in the frameless boats.

Mark out all the frame members. These can be traced with the aid of carbon paper if the drawings show either the whole frame full size or half the frame full size. Otherwise the drawings must be scaled up to full size on the requisite pieces of wood.

The number of frame members can easily add up to twenty or more separate pieces, and it is very easy to get them mixed up. It is therefore a good idea to devise some simple system of identification. I always use coloured sticky tape or labels and stick a piece of the same colour to all the components of one frame.

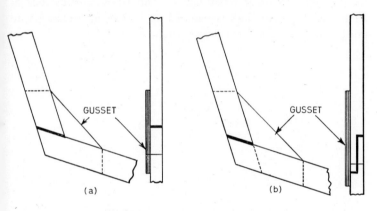

Frame with butt joint and plywood gusset

Frame with halved joint and ply-wood gusset.

Fig. 28

It is quicker and more accurate to work right through one operation, i.e. to cut out all the frame members before starting to assemble them. This applies all the way through the construction.

Shape the frame members in pairs if any curved sides are needed, i.e. both side members of the same frame together and both bottom members, to ensure similarity.

Cut the notches out to take the chines, gunwales, hog, and stringers, if anything slightly under size. Frame members are lap- or butt-jointed, supported by a ply gusset. These joints must be square and accurately cut to ensure a strong joint (see Fig. 28).

Cut the gussets from a sheet of $\frac{3}{16}$ in ply. Be careful to cut them so that they really are from a waste part of the sheet. This will entail roughly marking out the planking on the ply sheets.

If the boat you choose has bulkheads fitted to give buoyancy (the Graduate is one), the assembly of the frames is simplified if the bulkheads are fitted to the frames at this stage. So the ply for the bulkhead should now be cut out to the drawing. The waste from it will probably do for the gussets for the other frames. There is obviously no need for a gusset where there is a bulkhead.

If you are thinking of fitting a bulkhead which is not shown on the drawing, you must make up your mind now. Fitting it at a later stage when the hull is planked up is difficult, because you must ensure that the joint is water-tight.

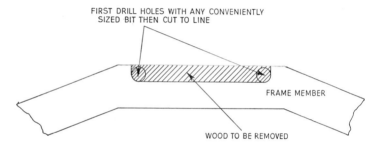

Fig. 29. Shaping frame to fit round hog.

When all the components are ready for assembly, assemble them 'dry', without glue. Check the measurements and fit any cross battens that are recommended in the design to hold them rigid. When you are satisfied that the frames are accurate, dismantle them and assemble them again with glue, screws, and/or nails as the case may be. Lay them flat on a true surface and check for accuracy again. It is advisable to have some weights handy, such as bricks, in case any part of the frame tends to 'lift'.

The accuracy of the frames is vital to the accuracy of the whole boat. Wipe off any surplus glue when it is in the rubbery stage, having left it partially to dry; it can then be scraped off quite easily. Some instructions advocate wiping off at once with a wet rag, but it is very easy to wipe the glue into the wood instead of off it. This does not matter on a surface that is to be painted, but the glue will show through varnish.

The inside edges of the hog are likely to be radiused. They look better so, and the joint rests firmer in the notches in the frames. A convenient method of cutting these radiused notches is shown in Fig. 29. Having marked out the notches, bore out to obtain the required radius, then saw out the waste with a coping-saw. This can be done, if preferred, before the frame members are assembled.

Some *transoms* are built up on frames as already described. They are then faced with $\frac{1}{4}$ or $\frac{3}{8}$ in ply according to the instructions on the drawing. For this process be careful to cut the notches for the chines, gunwales, and the hog in the frame only and not through the ply. If you fail to do this, these joints will not be concealed when the hull is planked up. The transom frame will have lap or butt joints for the side members and a centre member to take the transom knee and the rudder fittings. If nails are needed for securing the ply to the frame, make certain that the heads are punched just below the surface of the ply to allow for the stopping if the transom is to be painted.

If mahogany planking is specified for the transom and you cannot obtain a plank wide enough, the wood may have to be joined. For this plane the edges to be joined dead true, then glue and clamp with sash clamps, making sure that the wood does not bow. If it persists in bowing, clamp it flat across the grain at each end by means of one G clamp and two pieces of wood. If sash clamps are not readily available, screw two pieces of wood 2 × 2 in to the floor parallel to one another the distance of the width of the transom apart plus 1 in. Cut two wedges, put a strip of greaseproof paper in to prevent the transom from sticking to the floor where the join will come. Glue up the two pieces of the transom, lay it flat on the floor up against one 2 × 2 in, and knock in the wedges between the opposite edge and the remaining 2 × 2 in. If it bows, put a good heavy weight in the middle.

Mark out the shape of the transom and cut to size.

Knees are best cut out with a coping-saw (see Fig. 30). When planing the straight edges plane with the grain. Round the other edges with a spoke-shave to make a neat job. Some boats have only one knee, which should be cut in the same way.

There are a number of variations in the design of the *stem*; none of them are difficult. If the stem is made from one piece of wood, the ends of the chine and gunwales are bevelled and screwed and glued to the stem. If the stem is in two pieces, the chines and gunwales are notched into the inner stem or apron. I would like to mention here that there is no difference between an inner stem and an apron. It will be seen in Stage II that the fitting of the chines and gunwales is much easier in a boat which has a double stem.

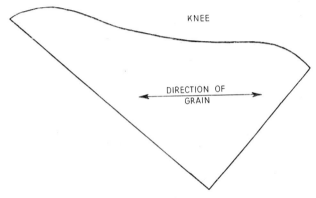

Fig. 30. The correct lie of the grain in a knee.

(*b*) Assembly of Components

Mark off the floor according to the drawing. You should do this whether you are building on an ordinary wooden floor or on a false floor out of doors. The false floor should of course be designed to suit the ground plan shown on the drawings. A centre-line must be marked first. On a false floor this is best done by nailing a long batten down the whole length of the floor. It must be absolutely straight.

On an ordinary boarded floor in a house one can often use the join of two boards for the centre-line. Otherwise use a length of chalked string pulled taut. Lifted a few inches off the floor, then released, this will leave a straight line, and is a method often recommended. I prefer something more permanent, so I draw a centre-line thickly in pencil using a chine as a guide.

Now mark off the station lines for the positions of the frames, ensuring that they are laid off at right angles to the centre-line. Check the diagonals with a piece of string or a lath. If the diagonal measurement between the legs of two frames, measured from the same position on the frames, is the same, all is well. This is a simple method of checking that the angles in a square or rectangle are 90 degrees, if you have no carpenter's square large enough.

The frames must be spaced exactly as laid down on the drawings. Note particularly that the forward frame will be shown in front of the station line, whereas the others will be aft of their station lines.

With one or two exceptions drawings and instructions are very sparing with their suggestions for the use of struts for the frames. To the beginner the frames, even when secured to the hog and keel, will seem very shaky. At least one strut should be used for each frame, from the floor to the top of the frame just below the notch for the hog. These struts must be screwed, not nailed, in position. Even if secured in this manner the frame at the chine joint will still tend to be flimsy. The frames must be vertical. A builder's plumb-line is a great help, or this simple substitute can be made: clamp a carpenter's square to a suitable length of planed wood which has at least one end square, with the thick side of the square in the horizontal plane. Stand the wood up against the frame and lay a spirit-level on the arm of the square. The square must be clamped to the wood at right angles. This produces a very effective means of checking the vertical position of the frames.

The drawings will either include in the side members of the frames enough wood to form the legs, which are to be fitted to the floor, or they will indicate where additional pieces should be fitted to the frames to form the legs.

The frames are screwed to the floor by means of small blocks of wood screwed to the leg and to the floor. The end of each leg must be square and rest on the floor to keep the frame true.

Setting Up Transom, Stem, and Hog

The transom and bow transom (for boats which have one) must be fitted with the knees. In some cases the stem piece is fitted with a knee. Be careful that the screws holding the knee to the transom are clear of where the rudder fittings will be screwed to the transom.

The transom is screwed to the floor in the same manner as the frames. In some boats the transom is not set up vertical but inclined inwards towards the next frame; so the distance from the bottom of the transom to the next frame will be less than the distance from the top of the transom to the frame on the line of the gunwale. It is important that two struts be fitted to the transom, one on each side.

There are three main methods of securing the hog, keel, and stem together:

1. The keel and hog can be glued and screwed together, and then the stem can be screwed to them. This type of assembly is the most difficult to fit to the frames, because of the force required to bend the assembly to fit them into the notches in the frames and transom. The maximum stress will be imposed on the frames and transom. When set up the ply planking butts up to the keel.

2. The hog can be fitted to the stem and fitted to the frames and transom. The keel is then laid over the hog and screwed to it. Again the ply planking is butted to the keel. The fact that the hog is fitted first, followed by the keel, simplifies the operation considerably.

3. The hog is fitted as in (2), but the ply planking is butted together over the hog and then the keel is laid on the ply. This probably is the easiest method of all.

Leave the stem and hog assembly to harden off for at least 24 hours before carrying on with Stage II. If need be, the stem and hog can be assembled together before the frames so that there is no delay after the frames are set up.

(c) Frameless Boats

The only components that need be constructed if you are building from drawings are the transom and the stem, unless you are going to build your own temporary frames. It is better to hire or borrow these because, when the boat is made, they are no good for anything else.

When you are building from a kit, the frames are supplied on loan or hire, usually for a deposit, which is refunded when they are returned in good condition. Take care of them. These frames already have notches cut for the chines and gunwales. Some drawings give details of how these frames are built up for the benefit of the boat-builder who is supplying his own frames.

The frames are set up as described in (b). Small blocks are screwed to the frames under the notches for the chines, hog, and gunwale, which are temporarily screwed to these blocks.

(d) Ply Clinker-built Boats

These are started in the same way as the frameless boat, but combine the permanent bulkheads which are treated in the same way as a normal frame. The main difference occurs in the planking of the hull.

CONSTRUCTION – STAGE II

(*a*) **There are no parts to be constructed at this stage.**

(*b*) **Assembly and Fitting of Chines, Gunwales, Hog, and Stringers (where applicable) to the Frames and Transom.**

Before going on to the details of assembly I propose to deal with the question of fairing-off and fairing-in. Most of these two processes go on at this stage. Both words are universally used as terms for shaping the main timbers to conform with the curves required for the correct shape of the hull. There are two lots of curves which need shaping – the longitudinal curves from the transom to the stem and those from the gunwales to the keel. From the plans you will see that these curves alter throughout the length of the boat. For example, the forward edges of the frames forward of the maximum beam will be faired-off so that their edges form a smooth curve. In the same way the frames aft of the maximum beam are faired-off on the aft edges. This also applies to the transom.

The chines, gunwales, and stringers are faired-in to the notches in the frames. The edges of the hog and chines are faired-off to obtain the correct transverse curves from hog to gunwale. It will be seen that the maximum fairing-off takes place on the frame next to the stem. When you start fairing-off, go very carefully. Wood taken off a frame cannot be put back. If you should cut too deeply when fairing-in to a frame notch, the gash can be packed out by a small piece of wood or ply; but be sure to trim it to the sides of the frames before finally gluing and screwing the chine or gunwale into position.

Sharpen all the tools to be used before you start any fairing, and set the plane iron as fine as possible. A spoke-shave and Surform file will be useful, and a coping-saw too for cutting into the notches and trimming their sides in cases where they have been left undersize. The remaining aids are a long lath and a steel straight-edge or 2-ft steel rule. These should be used as rules or path-finders. The lath must be long enough to bridge three frames and can be sprung to assimilate any desired curve. It must make complete contact with any surface it touches. The rule or straight-edge is used for checking the flat surfaces (see plate 29). It is a good plan to plane or sand one side of the lath as they usually have rough surfaces. An ordinary building lath will do, costing only a few pence.

To return to the assembly, building instructions vary in their recommendations for the fitting of the hog assembly to the frames and transom. The two main alternatives are:

1. You can screw the hog to the transom knee and fair-in the frame notches for the hog, working forward from the transom. Then glue and screw the hog to the frames and screw the stem to the floor.
2. You can screw the stem to the floor first, fairing-in the hog to the frame notches, working aft to the transom. After cutting the hog to length, glue and screw the hog to the frames and the transom.

In kits that supply the hog cut to length the first method is to be recommended. If you are using a kit where the hog is supplied uncut or if you are building from drawings, the second method is preferable. In both cases it is advisable to assemble the hog to the frames 'dry' first, to ensure that it is properly faired-in to the notches before the final fixing with glue and screws.

If you are using the first method, take care that the stem comes down to the floor exactly on to the allotted mark. When boring the holes for the screws, do not forget to use the dowel guide to ensure that the holes are not bored too deep, or the joints will be weakened. When assembling any components 'dry', use steel screws a size or two smaller than those specified in brass. Brass is relatively soft and is easily damaged if the screws are taken in and out for trial purposes.

Whichever method is used for fitting the hog, it is most important that cramps be used for holding the hog down in each notch while the holes are being bored, and again for the gluing and screwing. Considerable force, depending on the curvature of the hog called for in the plans, may be required to spring the hog down. It is therefore important that there should be a clamp to each frame notch. Under no circumstances try to pull the hog down into the notches by the screws, unaided by a clamp. You will probably break the screw and fail to get the hog well and truly seated in the notch.

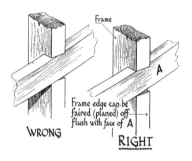

Fig. 31. Right and wrong way of fairing-in a cross member.

(*Courtesy: Bell Woodworking Co. Ltd*)

Take care when clamping the end of the hog to the transom knee. The knee will already have been shaped and cleaned; and the clamp jaw will cut into the knee and spoil the look of it, particularly if there is no aft decking to hide it. Tack a small piece of wood on to the knee temporarily to protect it.

For certain designs it will now be necessary to fit the keel to the hog (see Chapter VIII, p. 106). This is a straightforward job. In the case of a kit the centre-board slot may have been roughed out by the supplier: this is a great advantage. If there is no indication, it is advisable to mark the position out roughly before fixing the keel down. Note where the screws will come, or when you come to cut out the centre-board slot you may find some screws in the way which may break off in the hole.

Now follows the fairing-in of the chines, followed by the gun-wales. It does not matter which chine you fit first, provided that the second one is the opposite facing chine. In other words, for a double-chine boat do not fit both chines on one side before fitting a chine on the other side, as the hull may be distorted. Before beginning to fair-in the chines to the frame notches, take a good look at Fig. 31 which shows the right and wrong way of fairing-in to a frame and Fig. 32 shows the correct fitting for the transom joint. Begin with the transom joint, which will entail cutting a blind rebate in the transom. If the transom is made of ply fixed

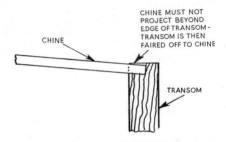

Fig. 32. Section of Chine-Transom joint.

to a frame there is no difficulty, as the rebate will have started as a notch cut in the frame before the ply was screwed to it. If you have a solid transom, the rebate is best cut out with a really sharp chisel. It will help if the transom is partially faired-off first.

It is most important that the chine be set deep enough in the transom, or too much will have to be faired-off the chine so that it may become too thin to take the screws for securing the plank-ing. Run a pencil-line therefore down the centre of the chine to indicate the point at which the planking will join.

With the first join completed, fair-in the notch in the frame next to the transom and repeat the same process on all the frames. Always clamp the chine into the notch that is ready when offering up the chine to the next one. At this point you being to feel a bit anxious about the rigidity of the frames. In that case there is no harm in fitting another temporary strut at any weak point.

You may find the chine difficult to bend; then the chine should be steamed. This is a simple operation for such small pieces of timber. Fig. 33 shows a simple steaming device. Use a length of galvanized water-pipe. Plug one end with a piece of wood, and bore a hole in the centre to take the spout of an electric kettle. The plug should be about 1 in thick and held in position by screws through the pipe. Place the wood in the pipe and lightly pack the open end with rag. As a rough guide for steaming time, calculate one hour for every inch of thickness of the wood plus half an hour.

Fig. 33. Sketch of simple steaming equipment.
(*Courtesy: Bell Woodworking Co. Ltd*)

With the first chine screwed up 'dry' to the frames, the tiresome business of fitting the forward end to the stem has to be carried out as follows:

1. Fitting to an apron or inner stem.

   This is relatively easy as the stem is already notched. The notches only have to be faired-in to take the chine. The surplus wood at the end of the chine can be cut off when the gluing and the screwing have been completed. This piece of spare wood can be used to tie the chine into position if you are short of clamps; in fact, it will probably do the job better than clamps owing to the angle. If you secure the chine by tying it in position while the glue is drying, be very careful not to pull the string too tight or the chine will bulge out of shape between the stem and the next frame.

2. This method is rather more difficult as the end of the chine has to be cut to lie against the stem and requires a compound bevel. It is probable that the chine may need twisting to conform with the lines required, and it will have to be held in this position while the glue is setting to prevent the joint from opening before the glue sets. This can be done quite simply by securing a clamp to the chine and using it to twist the

22. Bell Angler's Dinghy

23. Bell Angler's Dinghy under construction

24. *Osprey Mark II*

25. *Spitfire*

26. *'Yachting World' 13 ft Runabout*

chine and secure by cord. You must make sure that the clamp is really tight on the chine. The bevel joint is best finished to the final fit by use of a Surform file.

When this last joint has been completed, the chine can be glued and screwed up. It is important that these members be left for 24 hours to dry out thoroughly before any further work is carried out on them. All the chines are fitted in the same manner, and followed by the gunwales. The joints fixing the chines and gunwales to the transom and stem are of special importance, and great care must be taken to ensure that they are accurate. Otherwise it is impossible to fit the ply planking to lie smoothly and symmetrically.

Some designs call for intermediate stringers between the chine and the hog as an additional support to the floors. They are easy to fit compared with the chines and gunwales as they do not run the full length of the hull and are joined to the stem. Therefore fair them in like the chines.

On hard-chine boats it is likely that the chine will have a rebate cut in it (see plate 29). The planking will come up to the edge of this rebate, and a chine fillet or bone-piece will be fitted to act as protection to the edges of the ply. So when screwing the chine finally into position it is most important that the screw heads should be below the V of the rebate, or they will foul the bone-piece.

If you are building from drawings this rebate can be difficult to cut. It can be cut with the chine clamped down to a bench with a rebate plane in the normal way; but it is unlikely that many people will have a bench that is long enough to take a 12- or 14-ft chine. I found it quite satisfactory to fit the chine permanently to the frames, and cut the rebate with the plane when the bottom plank has been fitted. You use the edge of the plank as a guide. If you use this method, check carefully that the screws are deep enough to avoid fouling the plane. You may need to apply a second counter-bore to take the head of the screw down to the required depth.

When all the chines and gunwales are fitted the fair-off begins in earnest. On double-chine and hard-chine boats that do not have a rebated chine, draw a pencil-line down the centre of each chine. This is the guide for the position of the butt-joint of the planking.

Fair-off methodically. Do not hop about from one part to another. Work evenly down the length of one chine, then work down another, using a plane. Work with the grain where possible, particularly on the frame members and the chines. You will find mahogany easier to work than silver spruce. Take off a little at a time and repeatedly check the work with the lath or straight-edge. If any screws have been left proud and they foul the plane or spoke-shave, use the Surform file. It will remove both wood and metal without any bother.

Examine all the joints to see if there is any glue which has escaped being wiped off. Chip it off with a sharp chisel, finishing off with a scraper. If you leave this glue to be removed when the boat is planked up, it will be twice as hard to shift. It is well worth while to sand down the chines and gunwales at this stage. Start with a middle 2 grade and finish off with a fine one, always working with the grain.

(c and d) Frameless Boats and Clinker Ply.

Gunwales, chines and stringers are fastened at the stem, transom and permanent frames where applicable as in (a and b). For temporary frames they are screwed ONLY to a block on the frame from the inside. The temporary frames are removed when the hull is completed.

The notches for the hog, chines, and gunwales are already cut and do not require any fairing-in. Before fitting the hog, sight down the notches to see that the frames have been set up in line.

Notch the transom for the hog, then screw and glue it into position. Spring the hog down into the notches in the frames. The hog is then screwed to the frames at each notch from the inside through the block on the frame. Use steel screws.

The stem is secured to the floor in the same manner as before. The chines are fitted in the same way starting with the transom, each being screwed to its frame with the block provided. Then the gunwales are fitted.

There is much less fairing-off in this type of boat because

nothing is taken off the frames. Special care should be taken if you are using a 'one shot' glue. If the glue should ooze on to the temporary frame, you may find the frame hard to remove. Some people grease the frames lightly to safeguard against this. The same is likely to happen to a lesser extent if you use Aerolite. The hardener or glue will not stick unless you have applied it to the frame and to the member to be glued. So there is a distinct advantage in using a glue with a separate hardener on this type of boat.

CONSTRUCTION – STAGE III

PLANKING THE HULL

(a) Cutting the Hull Planking if Building from Drawings

If you have built your own frames and used ply gussets, you will have at least partially marked out the ply sheets for the hull planking or panels. This process should now be completed as accurately as possible. It entails plotting the shape of the ply panels on the ply sheets. The bottom panels, particularly the forward ones, are the most difficult as the drawings will probably not show them flat as they should be drawn out; so the curves due to the twist at the stem are hard to plot. I suggest you leave as much as you can as spare without interfering with the other panels. Leave, say, 8 in at the stem and 4 or 5 in on the sides for the first panel only. Saw out the panel and offer it up to the frames and chines.

Mark on the underside how much can be cut off to bring it to a reasonable size for final shaping to the hog and chines. Do the same on the opposite side of the boat. The first panel of each pair can be used as a pattern for its opposite. If you prefer, templates can be made of thick paper for the panels. Keep on trimming the templates until they fit; then lay them on the ply sheet and mark round them, leaving the ply panel oversize.

The aft panels are much easier to deal with. The ply sheet can usually be held up to the boat and marked off on the inside. All the ply sheets will have the British Standards Specification number stamped on them somewhere. See that this does not show on the boat as it is almost impossible to sand it off.

(b) **Planking up the Hull**

There are various alternative methods of planking up the hull, which I shall describe under separate headings.

1. *Joining Planking End to End*

If the boat is longer than the standard sheet of ply, i.e. 8 ft, the ply panels will have to be joined end to end, and you must decide now how this is to be done. The methods are:

(a) By a scarf joint (see Fig. 34).
(b) By a butt joint (see Fig. 35).

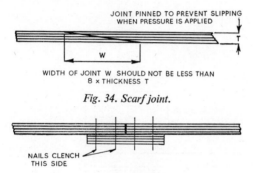

Fig. 34. Scarf joint.

Fig. 35. Butt joint.

Scarf joints are preferable if properly made. They are not easy to manage, though they can be applied by amateurs. The disadvantage of this method is that it considerably lengthens the panels, which have to be glued and screwed to the frames and longitudinals in approximately twenty minutes. This is a very important consideration if you are working on your own.

For scarf joints the ends to be joined are bevelled to a feather edge. The length of the bevel must be at least eight times the thickness of the ply. The bevelled faces are then glued together and held under pressure with pressure bars, which have a slightly convex surface to ensure even pressure. To prevent the two halves from slipping when pressure is applied, pin the two halves together with two or three panel pins, obtainable from a model shop. To prevent the glue sticking to the pressure bars, lay a piece of greaseproof paper over each joint (see Fig. 36). Sand the joint well before fitting the panel to the boat. The best way to cut the bevel is to

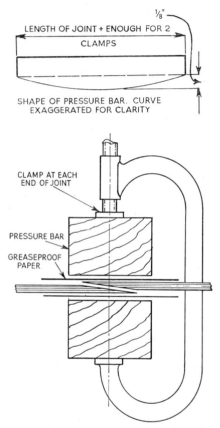

Fig. 36. *Method of using pressure bars for making a scarf joint.*

clamp the wood on to a trestle, aligning the end of the ply with the edge of the trestle; then plane the bevel with a short smoothing plane, ensuring an absolutely flat surface.

The butt joint is relatively simple. The panel ends are butted together and supported by a backing strip; this can be either a strip of ply or a suitable piece of mahogany. The joint is glued and drilled for two staggered rows of nails which are driven through the panel and the backing strip, and clenched over on the inside. The backing strip should be let into the hog and the chine or the chine and the gunwale, as the case may be (see plate 30). Some drawings do not specifically say that the backing strip should be let into the longitudinal members, but the joint is improved if it is.

If the butt-joint method is adopted the backing strip must be let in at this stage. The butt joint is the stronger of the two but the scarf joint is strong enough and looks much neater, as with the butt joint the clenched nails on the backing strip are bound to show.

2. Merits of Screwing or Nailing Planking

The main purpose of the screws and nails is to hold the planking in position while the glue is setting. Some instructions specify screws for all the planking: some say nails and screws. Screws must be used in any place where there is especial stress to be overcome, e.g. for fastening the bottom plank to the stem, and probably the remaining planks to the stem as well. The screws are likely to be longer than those used for the flatter areas.

I favour screwing the planking throughout, for the following reasons:

(a) I do not like the look of rows of clenched nails showing in the boat.

(b) A beginner finds it easier to make a good job by screwing than nailing.

(c) If you are working single-handed without help, you cannot reach to hold an iron against the head of the nail with one hand, while you clench over the end of the nail with a hammer in the other hand.

(d) Once the holes are bored for the screws, it takes the in-experienced builder less time to screw the panel into place than to nail it.

Against these arguments you can set the question of price. Nails are cheaper than screws; but they are also noisier, which is a consideration in a semi-detached house.

3. Nailing Planking

First take a good look at Fig. 37. This shows nails being driven through planking for clenching, also nails driven dead into a frame or deck beam where the nail point does not come through the

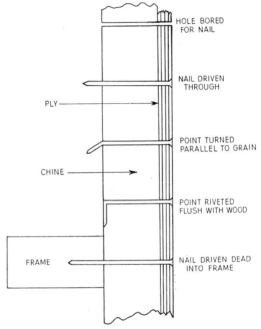

Fig. 37. Driving nails both dead and clenched.

wood. For clenching, drive the nails through and cut the point off, leaving approximately $\frac{3}{8}$ in still protruding. Hold an ordinary flat iron or a heavy hammer, such as a 2-lb club hammer, against the head. Turn the point of the nail parallel to the grain and rivet flush with the plank. It is imperative that the iron be held hard against the head, or the act of riveting will push the nail back and the head will then be proud of the panel. The nail heads can be sanded flush with the plank surface and painted. Great care must be taken not to bruise the panels when nailing; but you must work fast because of the glue, and your hammering must be accurate.

I consider that the paint 'takes' better if the head is punched just below the surface. The gap can be filled with brushing cement as a filler; this in turn can be sanded down in the normal way. This method is worth the extra trouble it involves. After turning the point of the nail you drive the head just below the surface with a centre-punch which has the point ground down to fit the head of the nail. Finish the riveting and hold the punch against the head of the nail with an iron or heavy hammer. Holes for the nails must be bored as described in Chapter III.

4. Screwing Planking

Chapter III, which deals with fastenings, gives details of hole sizes for the bore and counter-bore for different sizes of screws. This is repeated on the inside of the dust cover, you can tear this out and stick it on the wall, where it will be handy for reference. Fig. 38 shows the profile of the correct bore and counter-bore. The depth of the holes is most important, so cut some lengths of

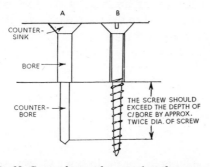

Fig. 38. Correct bore and counter-bore for screws.

dowelling to the length of the drill protruding from the drill chuck, less the depth of the hole required, and bore a hole down the centre of it. Slide the dowel down the drill to the chuck, and check the length protruding. Cut a separate piece of dowel for each size of screw and depth of hole that will be required.

The screws for planking are likely to be ¾ in No. 6 except for the stem. It is not always necessary to counter-sink them. If the hull is going to be varnished and the heads sanded flush with the planking, the screws will probably pull down without counter-sinking. If the chines are silver spruce, which is relatively soft, you may strip the hole so that the screw will not hold, so try one or two screws first. If they are not gripping, just touch the hole with the counter-sink bit. If the hull is being painted on the outside, it is better to counter-sink all the holes and fill them with stopping or brushing cement. This question is discussed fully in the chapter on finishes.

5. *Fitting the Bottom Planking*

The panels for planking will be slightly oversize if they are supplied in a kit. These should now be trimmed to a good fit and marked out for the holes for screws or nails.

Always begin with the forward bottom plank. This is of course the true bottom plank of the boat when the boat is the right way up, or the uppermost plank when it is upside down.

If you have decided to butt-join the panels, make sure that the ends to be joined are square. Clamp the forward panel to the framework, butting it up to the keel. With a small block of wood as a guide, make a pencil mark assimilating the line of the keel. The ply should protrude over the stem at this stage. Saw along the line and offer it up to the keel again. It may be necessary to bevel the forward edge a little to make a snug fit. The chine edge of the panel should still project beyond the chine. If the design requires the keel to be fitted after the planking is completed, the bottom planks are butted together on the hog; this is, in fact, a simpler process.

Bore six or eight holes for the locating screws and screw up the panel into position by these locating screws. Space them out as evenly as you can. At the stem you will have difficulty in pulling down the panel with screws alone, so use two or three clamps as well.

With some boats the twist on the panel at the stem can be tire-some; so locate it on the hog and chine, and work forward. If the panel is too obstinate and will not twist enough, pour a kettle of boiling water over the offending area and try again; it may need more than one dose. If slopping hot water on the floor is frowned on, take the panel off and put the end in a bath of hot water for about twenty minutes. Then offer it up again, clamp it in position, screw it with the locating screws, and leave it to dry off. Draw round the chines, frames, and hog on the underside, draw a ring round the locating screws, then bore and counter-bore for the screws, and for the nails, if necessary. You may have to counter-sink the screws. The distance between the screws or nails will be shown on the drawings or instructions. They will be closer to-gether nearer the stem because a greater strain has to be overcome as a result of the twist in that area. The screws in the stem will be longer than those used for the rest of the panel.

Get ready the screws, nails, and all the tools for finally screwing up the panel. You must aim at having the panel glued and screwed in about twenty minutes from the time the glued surfaces are brought together. The same applies whether you are using a 'one-shot' glue or the two application method. Before starting make sure that any rough surfaces resulting from boring the holes are removed. Spread the glue on the frames, chines, and hog with a thin piece of ply or a short stiff bristled brush. If using a one-shot glue, apply the glue to both surfaces, using the lines drawn on the underside of the panel as a guide. If you are employing the two application method, spread the hardener on the panel with a brush; two coats may be needed if the hardener soaks in too quickly. Place the panel in position, screw in the locating screws, then start at the aft end of the panel and work forward, screwing or nailing as you go. It is a good plan to put in every other screw or nail, then go back and put in the remainder afterwards. Some help, skilled or unskilled, is very welcome at this stage. Apart from assistance in screwing, it is very handy to have someone standing by to pick up the box of screws you have dropped or find the lost screwdriver. Of course, if the panel is being nailed, you must have some help in clenching the nails.

Remember to wipe off the surplus glue. If the panel is to be butt-joined to the aft panel, the supporting strip should be glued as well. Now drill for the nails in two staggered rows, nailing from the outside and clenching over on the inside. Wipe the remaining glue from the other half of the strip very thoroughly.

Having completed the first plank, fit the opposite panel on the other side. Then follow with the bottom aft panels, which are quite straightforward. Make sure that they are butted up tight to the end of the forward panel and work aft from the butt joint to the transom. Finally nail up to the backing strip.

6. Finishing the Planking of the Hull

There are three types of joint on the chine between the bottom and side panels – Bevel, Lap, and Fillet (see Fig. 39).

Bevel Joint. This is the most common type of joint on double-chine boats. Bevel joints are not difficult to manage, but they demand care and accurate workmanship if a good job is to be made.

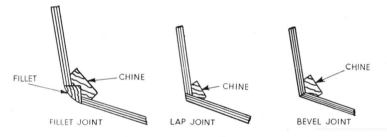

Fig. 39. Fillet, lap and bevel joint on the chine.

The chine edge of the panel should just overlap the centre-line of the chine. When wiping off the surplus glue from the chine after fitting the bottom panel, scrape the chine thoroughly clean of glue. With a rebate plane, bevel this edge for the full length of the chine except for the last 15 in or so at the stem, where on some boats the bevel turns into a butt joint. Be careful not to cut into the chine when planing the bevel. If the surplus glue has not been properly wiped off, the plane is blunted and planing becomes difficult.

Lap Joint. This is the easiest joint except where the joint changes from lap to bevel towards the stem. The drawings will indicate where the change takes place. The joint will have to be cut with a chisel, but on each side of the change of joint the panel can be planed. A smoothing plane should be used for the lap joint and a rebate plane for the bevel.

Fillet Joint. The cutting of the rebate in the chine has already been covered in the previous chapter. The fitting of the fillet or bone-piece cannot be completed until the side panels are fitted. All you have to do at this stage is to plane the edges of the bottom panel back to conform to the rebate in the chine. It is imperative that the 90-degree angle of the rebate is not increased, or the fillet will be a loose fit. So plane very carefully.

Fitting the side panels is straightforward, and the same procedure should be followed. It will be a great deal easier at the stem, although the strain will still be greater than farther aft.

The bevel joint requires patience more than anything else. Few amateur builders have at their disposal a bench with vices that can hold a ply panel upright while it is being planed along the edge. A simple method of doing this is to stand two trestles end to end and screw a piece of wood either along the top or the side to keep them rigid. Lean the panel up against the trestles with the side to be planed uppermost. The panel can usually be clamped to the trestles; this will give a rigid support to hold the panel for planing. The bevel must be accurate and conform to its counterpart on the bottom panel already on the boat. Use a smoothing plane, and plane with long strokes to keep the edges as level as possible. Take a little off at a time along the whole length and offer it up to the hull, marking where more planing is required: this may well entail offering up the panel three or four or more times for accuracy.

It is important that the joins on the ends of the side panels, either butt or scarf, should not be opposite those on the bottom panel. It looks much neater if two opposing panels on opposite sides of the hull have the joint exactly opposite.

Preparing a panel with a lap joint is simple. The change of joint towards the stem needs care. An alternative method is to leave the edge proud of the bottom panel, and plane it down afterwards when it has been glued and screwed into position.

The fillet joint also presents no problem as the edge of the side panel can be left proud of the rebate and planed back to the rebate when the panel is finally in position.

I would like to point out here that it is bad practice to have a scarf joint on a frame; it is better that it should be equidistant between two frames. Although some plans specify a butt joint on a frame it is preferable that it should be between two frames and supported by a backing strip.

When fitting the side panels you need not cut them to shape along the gunwale. You can do this much more easily when the boat is turned over, and you can see what you are doing. In double-chine boats the middle panel or bilge panel will be treated in the same way as the bottom panel when it comes to preparing the edge on the chine to take the topside panel.

With all the planking completed the overlapping edges on the transom and the stem should be trimmed off. The stem will have to be finished off according to the design. If it is a double-stem type, the outer stem should now be fitted. First the edges of the panels must be trimmed back to the apron or inner stem; then the outer stem must be trimmed off flush with the panels. The forward edge of the stem will probably be fitted with half-round brass banding after the boat has been painted, so try the banding at this point to make sure that the edge of the stem is exactly the right width for the banding.

If the drawings call for the keel to be fitted after the planking, it is important that the ply be cut away from the slots in the hog to take the centre-board. This must be done before the keel is fitted, otherwise you cannot line up the corresponding slots in the hog with those in the keel. In nearly all kits the hog and the keel are already slotted for the centre-board with probably one or two pieces of wood left to be cut out. The ply must be planed over the hog to form a flat surface to take the keel, if the keel is to be fitted over the planking.

If you are building from drawings only, I do not recommend your trying to cut the slots for the centre-board before fitting the hog and keel. You can do this operation when the keel is fitted in position provided you mark out the keel and hog accurately (see Chapter XI).

If the hull requires a chine fillet or bone-piece to be fitted, now is the time to fit it. If the bend is very severe it may need steaming.

The fillet will be glued and screwed into position and finally planed down to the panels, and then the edge rounded. Make sure therefore that the screw holes are countersunk deep enough so that they do not foul the plane when the fillet is being finished off. The screw holes will be filled with stopping before painting.

(c) Planking up Frameless Boats

The procedure for these boats is much the same except that the planking is not screwed or glued to the temporary frames.

(d) Planking up Clinker-ply Boats

These boats are planked up in the same sequence starting with the bottom plank and working up to the gunwales. The panels can be butt or scarf joined according to taste.

The main difference between this type of construction and the hard-chine and frameless boats is in the method of securing the panels to the stringers. The round-bilged hull is the reason for this.

Start by fitting the forward bottom panel. This is shaped to fit the hog, as already described. It is held in position with clamps and locating screws and is pressed down on to the stringer, which it must cover completely. On the underside of the panel draw a line with a pencil to show the amount to be cut away. Take off the panel and saw off the surplus so that the edge is flush with the top edge of the stringer (i.e. the topside when the boat is the right way up). Mark the holes to be bored for fixing to the hog, the bulkheads, the stem, and the stringers.

You should cut the panel to size at this stage because it is difficult to plane it down when it is finally glued and screwed to the chine. It must have a neat edge because it shows from the inside. The row of screws along the stringer must be on the keel side of the stringer. When the panel fits to your satisfaction, glue and screw it into place; then do the same with the opposite forward panel followed by the aft panels. It does not matter if the panels protrude beyond the transom or the stem as they can be trimmed to fit afterwards. You should now mark a line down the panel. The distance of this line from the edge of the stringer will be stated on the drawing. Usually the kits supply a marker made of ply. If they do not you can easily make one up or use an ordinary carpenter's gauge. Draw this line the full length of the boat from stem to transom. This edge is then bevelled from the line to the stringer. At each end the bevel turns into a gradually

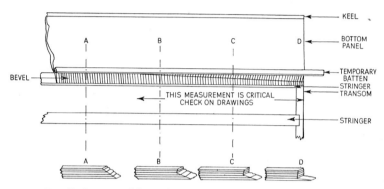

Fig. 40. Sections of diminishing rebate in Clinker-ply construction.

deepening rebate so that the panels butt at the stem and transom (see Fig. 40). The distance from the stem and transom where the rebate begins will be indicated on the drawings. It is sometimes important that this distance should be adhered to accurately so as to conform with the class measurement rule. The next panel, the bilge panel, overlaps this bevel as indicated in Fig. 40. Exactly the same procedure is followed in fitting the remaining panels.

XI

CONSTRUCTION – STAGE IV

Stage IV covers the completion of the hull with the hundred and one odd jobs it entails, leaving only the fittings, masts, spars, and rudder to be dealt with. They follow in the next chapter.

The hull is now planked up, but still secured to the floor upside down. One should take advantage of this to sandpaper the hull and finish it off now as far as possible. The work is so much easier when the hull is rigid. So sand the hull all over with the grain.

Some of the larger screws may have had to be counter-sunk deeper than was intended, and one or two of them may have broken off. Plug these holes with a piece of dowel and sand down to the skin surface. This is necessary if the heads of the screws are more than $\frac{1}{8}$ in below the surface, as it is inadvisable to rely on stopping to fill holes over this size.

I shall deal with the various tasks to be carried out item by item, including what must be done if you are building from drawings only. They boil down to straightforward carpentry in most cases. The sequence of these tasks will vary from boat to boat, and some of them will not apply to the boat you have chosen.

Turning the Boat Over

Before beginning to dismantle the hull from its supports, make two sets of chocks to support the hull when turned over. Cut them from odd scrap wood, the larger the better. Cut them so that they fit the hull in a particular place, then mount them on a stout board the width of the keel apart. Pad them with rubber covered with canvas. It is much easier to make them fit the hull upside down than to struggle under the boat when it is turned over.

Gather around you a small labour force. If she is a decked boat the hull will not yet be structurally complete, as the deck beams will not be in place. Apart from supporting the deck and possibly the mast these beams help considerably to strengthen the sides of the boat, so it is important that too great a strain should not be imposed by standing the boat on its sides at this stage.

The frame legs can be sawn off near the gunwale. The same applies to the stem support and to the transom except in cases where the legs are screwed on to the frames or in frameless boats. For the latter the frames are returnable and should therefore be looked after. Unscrew these from the floor. It is advisable to have some blocks or boxes to rest the boat on when she is released from the floor. Then lift her up and over to lie on the chocks already prepared.

On prams and similar small boats without decking the remaining tasks are few, consisting of fitting thwarts and any strengthening members required, such as quarter knees, and adding any intermediate floors and reinforcing pieces for the gunwales. All this is straightforward simple carpentry.

Deck Beams

With a decked boat there is plenty of work to be done. When she is chocked up securely and not wobbling, plane off the surplus ply above the gunwales. Mark the positions of the deck beams and check carefully that they are at right angles to the centre-line.

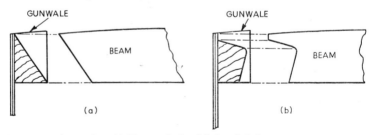

Fig. 41. Two methods of fitting deck beams.

The deck beams will be already shaped if they are supplied in a kit, otherwise they must be sawn and planed to shape according to the drawing. Leave them slightly oversize. On larger boats the deck beams are usually let into the gunwales by means of a dove-tail joint. Owing to the curve of the gunwales you must make a compound bevel as well. These joints can be considerably simpli-fied. Fig. 41 shows the two alternative methods of making the joint for the deck beam to the gunwale. Use whichever method suits the design in question.

Centre-board Case

In kits the centre-board case is supplied built up ready for fitting to the boat. Building it up from drawings is quite simple. The two sides are held apart by a spacing piece of wood at each end. Cut the two sides roughly to shape and clamp them together. Finish the bottom edge, which is located on the hog, with a spoke-shave and plane, taking care that the edges are kept square with the sides; otherwise the case will not stand vertical on the hog. Mark the exact position on the hog for the centre-board case.

To ensure that there are no high spots on the bottom edges, rub the edges with chalk and lay the centre-board on the hog. Press it down firmly. If the chalk line is transferred to the hog for the whole length of the case, all is well. If the line is broken or has patches where no chalk shows on the hog, these are the places where the centre-board is not touching on the hog.

When the bottom edges of the case fit the hog to your satis-faction, mark them so that they can be put together again in the same place. Make a mark also for the pivot bolt for the centre-board, and bore the hole exactly to size at 90° to the surface.

Take the sides apart, glue and screw one spacing piece to each side on the inside, then leave for the glue to harden off thoroughly. Give the insides three or four coats of clear Cuprinol as a preserva-tive. Glue and screw the two sides together. Wedge a piece of wood the same thickness as the spacers in the centre and leave it there until the case is fitted in the boat.

In a kit-built boat cut away the web of wood in the slot for the centre-board in the keel. Figs. 42 and 43 show two ways of fitting the centre-board case. Fig. 42 shows the way that is easiest, provided that you have a pair of steel sash cramps. Detachable

sash-cramp heads fitted to a wooden board will not do. Lay the
centre-board case on the hog in the right position, tack two short
lengths of lath or similar wood on the hog tight against each side
of the case and one short piece at one end (it does not matter which
end). Turn the boat over and support it on the trestles or boxes.
Remove the movable stops from the sash cramps and push the
bars of the cramps through the slot in the centre-board case, one
at each end with the tension end at the top of the case.

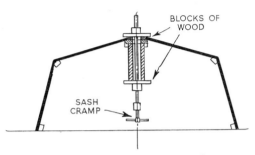

*Fig. 42. Method of fitting centre-board casing using sash cramp to draw centre-
board case into position.*

Push the case up into position with the bars protruding through
the slot in the keel, and get some help to fit the heads back on the
cramp bars. Tighten up the cramps. This will draw the case into
position within the laths tacked on the hog.

Bore, counter-bore, and counter-sink for the screw which will
hold the case in position. The screws required are likely to be
$2\frac{1}{2}$ to 4 in long and may be up to size 14. It is a help to run a steel
screw in a smaller size down each hole. Take down the case and
clean off the burrs caused by boring the holes.

The joint between the case and the hog must be water-tight and
is a constant problem. Prestik tape is a help. Kits that recommend
the use of Prestik will supply it in most cases. If you want to
obtain some, you may have difficulty in buying it retail. Prestik
Builders or Coachbuilders Sealing Strip can be used and is obtainable through wholesale merchants. The tape is supplied with
cellophane stuck to one side. Pull it off and lay it over the joint
on the hog. Make sure that it is even and does not overlap. Clamp

the centre-board case back into position with the sash cramps as before, grease the screws and screw up evenly all round. The Prestik tape never dries and will squash out all round the joint; trim with a razor blade. Tighten again in two or three days.

Fig. 43 shows a method of fitting the case if you do not own any sash cramps and cannot borrow them. Fit a temporary support between the gunwale amidships, screw a block on the floor, and

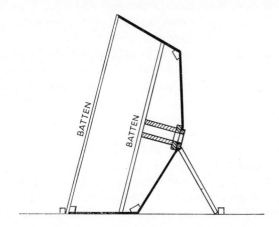

Fig. 43. Alternative method of fitting centre-board casing.

turn the boat on its side with the gunwale against the block. The side panel must be flat on the floor so that the weight is taken on the chine and gunwale. Put two supports under the keel, one aft and one under the bow. The centre-board case will have to be held in position until four or six screws are put in to hold it while the rest of the screw holes are bored. Nail a lath along the hog to locate the case on the hog, and use a batten tacked across the top of the case touching each side of the boat to ensure that the case is at right angles to the hog. Screw the case firmly into position with Prestik tape as already shown.

Centre-board

The centre-board is always supplied in kits already cut to size and shaped. It is often already fitted with friction pads, or they are supplied ready for fitting. This is true only of wooden centre-boards. As far as I know there are no kits which supply metal centre-boards, except for some of the moulded-hull boats.

The object of the friction pad is to keep the centre-board down against the natural tendency for it to float up. The friction device is fixed to the centre-board, and is a tight fit between the sides of the centre-board case. Plate 33 shows one friction device – a short length of hose is screwed to the centre-board, the screws being used for tensioning the hose, and two ply pads are fitted, one each side, to take any side play of the board in the case.

The alternative method is to fit Kautex pads. These are fitted on each side of the board and should be sanded to a tight fit.

Centre-boards are not difficult to make from drawings, particularly those made of ply. These are usually made from $\frac{1}{2}$ to $\frac{5}{8}$ in marine ply. Cut it out and bevel the edges according to the design. You can do this with a spoke-shave or Surform file.

A metal centre-board is a different matter altogether. If it is made of mild steel it must be plated. On our 'Yachting Monthly' Junior we fitted a $\frac{1}{4}$ in mild steel plate, cadmium plated, and it has proved a great success. It is of course heavy, weighing 45 lb. A metal board necessitates some hard work in shaping, unless you can get it flame-cut with an oxy-acetylene cutter.

The centre-board will pivot on a brass or gunmetal bolt, usually $\frac{3}{4}$ in in diameter. This will be secured each side of the case by a nut. It is a good plan to fit a rubber washer behind each nut to prevent water leaking through. Do the nuts up tight, but take care not to distort the sides of the case through overtightening.

Completing Inboard Fittings

It is a good rule that as much work on such things as side benches, thwarts, and supporting knees for the centre-board case should be done before the decking is fitted. The supporting knees should be cut in the same way as the transom knee.

If you are going to have a samson post, prepare it completely before you fit it.

The large plan at the end of the book shows the breast-hook and king plank. The king plank is rebated into the breast-hook. The aft end is rebated into the aft-deck beam, the intermediate deck beams being notched to take it. In some boats the king plank is not rebated to take the ply decking, and the two halves of the decking butt to each other on the king plank. If there are no coamings, the king planks fore and aft should be rebated into half of the deck beam only.

The carlines should now be fitted. They run parallel to the gunwale in most cases and support the inboard edges of the side decking. They will be rebated into the deck beams at each end of the cockpit. Be careful that they do not distort the beams by being too long. Being curved, they will have to be sprung into position, and their length must be accurate (see Figs. 59 and 60).

Bilge Keels or Rubbers

These are long battens glued and screwed to the underside of the hull on the bottom plank to give protection to the bottom plank when it is lying on the shore. The ends should be tapered down so that they cannot catch on ropes or weed.

Side Benches and Thwarts

There are so many variations of these that it is difficult to give details. The work involved is simple and straightforward, but take care to round the edges and corners well, and sand them thoroughly. Check that all screw heads are well counter-sunk so that there are no sharp edges to catch clothing.

When intermediate floors are fitted, make sure that the tops are level with the frame members. They are glued and screwed into position from the underside through the bottom hull panel.

Some boats, e.g. frameless boats, will have floor battens fitted instead of floorboards resting in frames. If the hull planking has been butt joined, these floor battens should be trenched to take the backing strip. This is much neater than cutting the battens and fitting each side of the backing strip.

Floorboards in boats with built-in frames should be secured by turn buttons to prevent them floating up if water swamps the boat. They should not be varnished but should be given two or three coats of clear Cuprinol.

The mast may be stepped on the hog or on the deck. Both methods are simple, but make sure that the bottom of the step block conforms with the heel of the mast as near as possible. Also allow ample clearance in the block. The mast should not be a tight fit. Dirt, sand, and water will get in whatever happens, and the mast may swell, making it difficult to step.

When the mast is stepped on the hog, the fore deck is usually recessed to take the mast. It is held in the recess by a movable batten or catch, and the whole is known as the mast gate.

Decking

Before starting to fit the decking, sand and clean the inside of the hull thoroughly. A vacuum cleaner is a good means of cleaning out the dust, but use a brush to loosen it. If there are to be drain plugs in the transom, it is easier to bore the holes now before the aft decking is fitted.

With the aid of a lath fair-off the deck beams to take the decking. This will entail fairing a little off the gunwales. It is a great advantage to put on the first two coats of varnish now because you can see what you are doing. Once the deck is fitted it is very easy to miss the odd patches under the deck, so apply the first two coats of varnish as explained in Chapter XII. This gives you the chance to varnish thoroughly the awkward places such as the deck beams and the stem.

Start by fitting the forward decking. If the king plank is rebated to take the panels, the ply should be glued and sanded along the rebate and nailed along the gunwale. The slots in the screw heads should be in line fore and aft for the sake of neatness, and the heads sanded flush with the decking. The nails should be driven dead into the gunwales. Copper boat nails can be used and sanded flush with the decking, but they do tend to tarnish and mark the ply even if varnished so it is better to use brass nails with a small head. Punch them slightly below the surface and fill with Brummer Green Label Mahogany Stopping. There is no need to nail along the deck beams; the glue alone will be enough.

The side decking will butt joint the fore decking but the deck beams will not be wide enough for the side decking and fore decking to be nailed down. Therefore fit a length of wood as a packing piece between the gunwales and carlines against the aft side of the deck beams. This allows for the side decking to be glued and nailed to it. The same will apply to the aft end of the side decking where the join will butt with the aft decking.

Sand down the decking carefully with the grain and trim the edges of the decking back to the planking. Fit the gunwale rubbers or rubbing strakes with glue and nails to the top edge of the rubbers slightly proud of the decking, about $\frac{1}{16}$ in. Use plenty of glue rubbed into the edges of the deck ply, but take care not to get it on the decking more than you can help. Wipe off the surplus glue carefully and thoroughly. Sand down the top of the gunwale rubbers level with the deck.

Fit the deck coamings fore and aft of the cockpit according to the drawings. If they are not included for the side of the cockpit, they are well worth fitting. They will make all the difference to the look of the boat. The carlines will be very conspicuous unless covered. They will need covering with $\frac{1}{4}$ in mahogany with the top edge rounded. These coamings can be glued into position without any screws; they should be held in position by clamps until the glue is dry. The coamings aft of the cockpit will cloak the joint of the king plank in the deck beam.

XII

FINISHES

When the hull is completed all ready for varnishing and painting, the launching day comes at last in sight; but on no account must you hurry the final stages. Although you are unlikely to obtain the perfect finish, it is well worth while to persevere and aim as high as you can.

You may have to move the boat out of the house before completing the painting and continue in the open but before you do this one or two coats of varnish should be put on the hull and at least one coat of primer. I propose to deal with varnishing and painting separately for the sake of continuity, but there is no reason why, to suit your own convenience, you should not stop the varnishing and change over to the painting and vice versa.

Before starting to paint or varnish the boat, it is a good plan to cover the whole craft in Cuprinol Sealer, inside and out, paying particular attention to the ends and edges of the ply panels. Cuprinol Sealer is a clear, water-repellent wood preserver which has only recently been put on the market. It will prove of great help in preserving the wood and minimizing the absorption of water, should the paint or varnish crack.

Allow five days for the solvent to dry out thoroughly before you start painting or varnishing. Do not sand the surface after the sealer has been applied. Any hairs that are left standing can be rubbed off with a coarse rag. Subsequent coats of paint or varnish can be rubbed down in the usual way, but if the sealed surface itself is sanded, its sealing properties will be destroyed. It should be remembered that any wood that has been treated with the sealer cannot be glued. While the sealer is admirable in every way for our purposes, it should never be used on boats of clinker or carvel construction where absorption of water is relied on to ensure the sea- or river-worthiness of the craft.

Varnish

There should not be a great deal of sanding to be done on the bare wood particularly if the ply used for the decking and hull is sapele-faced. This comes from the kit supplier or timber merchant with a smooth surface and will need little or no sanding. Also sand-paper can effect very little improvement on a well-planed surface, provided that your plane and other cutting tools were properly set and sharp. I have already mentioned in Chapter VII that compo-nents should wherever possible be prepared and sanded before fitting. So the only places likely to require sanding are the joint edges and the hole for the screws and nails. You will already have decided whether you intend to varnish the outside of the hull, or the transom and inside only, or the inside only.

A cork sandpaper block is by far the best implement to use for sanding. It costs no more than a shilling and is ideal in every way. Do not use a block of wood, because inevitably the edge will dig into the ply surface and score it. The cork block is soft, so that if you should bring it into contact with the wood as a result of the sandpaper tearing, you will not score the wood. Always sand with the grain, except of course on the edges of the ply where you must sand along the edge and not across it so as not to chip the outer skin.

There should be no need for the use of any coarse paper at all. I suggest 'middle 2' as a satisfactory grade to start with and a 'fine 1' for the final rub-down. Any trace of glue must be removed. If the hull is being varnished outside, clear any glue which may have entered the slot in the head, because the varnish will not 'take' over glue very satisfactorily. The screw heads will be burnished as you sand the hull, and the same is true of the nail heads in the decking. The latter are most important as they are always visible. The appearance of the deck will depend on how accurately you hammer the nails home.

It is well worth while examining the inside of the boat upside down if she has any decking. This will give you a chance to clean up the hidden surfaces. It is surprising what you will find – little drops of glue that have run and some nasty rough edges. Whether Cuprinol is used or not, it is most important that all the dust be removed, otherwise it will ruin the varnishing. The dust lies in all the nooks and crannies as well as lying on the surfaces. Wipe the whole boat over with a cloth damped in turpentine substitute. When this has dried off, brush the surface with a clean brush. A final wipe with a clean white rag will show if there is any dust left.

On the planking and other surfaces there should be no need for any filling beyond what results from rubbing on coats of varnish. If you feel that a gap between two planks is beyond filling with coats of varnish, ask your paint suppliers for a clear filler to suit the varnish you wish to use. The International Paint Co. and Messrs Cellon both supply a varnish filler. You must carry out their instructions most carefully.

Conditions

The ideal conditions for varnishing are extremely difficult for the amateur to achieve. Most people have to reach a compromise as near to the ideal as possible. The sanding and the subsequent rubbing down between coats should be done in a different room to the painting. This is of course asking for a lot; but you must remember that dust is most persistent stuff; it clings to walls and curtains, and it fills the cracks between the floor-boards. The least you must do after wiping the boat is to run over the floor with a vacuum cleaner and change your clothes.

If possible, wear clothes that are not woolly or fluffy, and sprinkle water on the floor. If you are working in the open, choose a sheltered part of the garden, preferably on grass. If you are confined to a draughty old garage, stuff up the cracks to stop dirt blowing about. Even in 1956, when the weather was bad, we had no difficulty in doing all the painting and varnishing in the garden except for the first two coats. We did the work on the drive and lightly watered the gravel before starting. Varnishing should never be undertaken after 3 p.m. in the open, even on the finest summer day. The evening dew will cause a 'bloom' to form on the varnish and spoil everything. Rubbing down, however, can be carried out at any time. It does not matter how early you start to varnish, provided the work is dry. In hot temperatures out of doors the boat should be shaded when the varnish is applied. Without free circulation of air the drying time of some varnishes is extended up to 50 per cent. You can achieve some movement of air in a room by using a vacuum cleaner.

Applying the Varnish

The first coat should be diluted in accordance with the manufacturer's instructions. The usual proportion is about 70 per cent varnish to 30 per cent turpentine. Use one of the modern synthetic varnishes. The two firms I mentioned above both offer an excellent product. Although the drying time of these varnishes is approximately four hours, you should allow twelve hours to pass before rubbing down a coat. When the first diluted coat is dry, rub some whitening all over it, applied dry on a rough rag or piece of hessian. Rub hard across the grain: this action removes all the hairs that have risen from the wood as the varnish dries. The whitening acts as a filler, but only for the small marks in the grain: do not attempt to use it for larger areas such as bad ply joints. Wipe off the surplus whitening gently across the grain with a soft rag damp with turpentine, especially from the corners by the chines and frames. Apply the second coat at full strength. Do not attempt long narrow stretches. When varnishing, cover the hull and decking systematically in areas about 3 ft square.

When you have covered a whole area, e.g. the decking, the varnished area must be smoothed out. This process is known as laying off. It is done to ensure that the coat is evenly distributed and to prevent running. Scrape the varnish from the brush and cover the area with up and down strokes, paying particular attention to the overlapping of the areas varnished and to the edges, corners, and recesses.

It is not generally necessary to rub the second coat down, unless it looks unsatisfactory when dry. You can now apply the third coat in exactly the same manner as the second. It should then be rubbed down with a fine grade of wet or dry paper used wet. Use plenty of water and rub the whole surface evenly. You can rub across the grain without marking. Keep rinsing the coat in the water. Wash off the worst dirt with clean water and, when dry, wipe over with turpentine on a clean rag. Again it is much easier with a hose pipe to wash out the inside of the boat when it is upside down. Apply the fourth coat. This will be the last one if all has gone well.

It is worth mentioning that Messrs Llewellyn Rylard Ltd, who supply an excellent range of marine paints and varnishes, supply varnish in collapsible tubes as well as in ordinary tins. These tubes are most convenient as you can keep a tube handy for touching up. The same firm supplies a similar cement filler.

Do's and Dont's for Brushes

1. Don't buy cheap brushes. This is false economy.
2. Don't leave a brush standing on its bristles, even in turpentine.
3. Don't use a new brush on a final coat. Break it in on undercoats.
4. Don't leave brushes lying about to collect dust. Wrap them in grease-proof paper.
5. Don't blame the brush or varnish for failures.

Paint

Much the same rules apply for painting as for varnishing. The sequence is as follows:

1. First coat of primer stopping and brushing cement.
2. Second coat of primer.
3. First undercoat.
4. Second undercoat.
5. Top coat of enamel.

Buy all your paints from the wide selection of marine paints offered by the manufacturers. Buy the same make throughout.

Primer

Primer is meant to soak into the wood as much as possible, so it is important that the decking and the transom, if you are varnishing it, should have two coats of varnish before you use primer on the hulls. If you prime the hull first and get some primer on the plain wood, you will find it very difficult to remove; but it can be rubbed off varnish fairly easily. Paint the whole area over evenly and leave for twelve hours. Primer tends to be fairly thick, so make sure you have mixed it thoroughly. Rub down all over with sandpaper, evenly and carefully.

Stopping

This is always a tedious job. Every nail and screw head must be carefully stopped. The stopping is a heavy putty-like substance and must be pressed into the holes with a putty knife or some other suitable instrument. It must be properly worked into the holes to ensure that the spaces are completely filled. Leave the stopping to dry hard. Rub it down with sandpaper, using the cork block, and perhaps go over it a second time. Make certain that the level of the stopping is slightly above the level of the surrounding wood. Very slight shrinkage usually takes place when the stopping dries.

Brushing Cement

If you find after rubbing down the stopping that there are some small scratches and fine lines that need filling, use Brushing Cement. This is a liquid stopping that is put on with a brush. Brush it over the affected areas. Let it dry hard and rub it down with a fine sandpaper.

Second coat of Primer

Paint over the whole area again with a second coat of primer. Some people advise you to put in stopping after this coat, but I disagree. Rub the coat over with fine sandpaper and wipe over with a rag soaked in turpentine.

Undercoat

Always use the correct undercoat for your final top coat of enamel. Paint the whole area over with undercoat and rub down with fine wet or dry. When it is clean and dry, repeat the process.

Top Coat of Marine Enamel

With this coat you make or mar the whole job. Dust is again the danger, so take all the precautions outlined for varnishing. Cover the whole area with even strokes and apply the coat generously. Brush the coat out well to avoid runs and finish with lighter strokes applied with the grain.

It does not matter much if the wood appears when you rub down the undercoat. Apply another coat if you feel that too large an area is showing. If you make a mess of the top coat, let it dry really hard and rub down well with wet or dry. All the shine must be removed before another coat is applied.

Remember to keep your brushes clean. Have clean jars and thinners handy and a few clean rags.

27. *Aquabat being towed for water skiing at 30 mph*

28. *Aquabat powered by British Seagull 40 Plus Outboard*

29. *A hard-chine hull under construction, being faired-off preparatory to fitting panels. The arrow indicates the rebate in the chine to take the chine fillet*

30. *Fitting a bottom panel to a hard-chine hull; note the backing strip for the butt joint of the panels, which is let into the hog, bilge stringer and chine*

XIII

MASTS, BOOMS,
RUDDERS, AND FITTINGS

There are many minor variations in both the Bermudian and Gunter rigs, as well as different types of drop and fixed rudder; and the various fittings will depend on the design of the boat. It is therefore impossible to deal with all the possible alternatives without becoming deeply involved in detail. I have tried to lay down the salient points of each item.

The Boom

Most booms will have a grooved track to take the bolt-rope on the foot of the mainsail. In kits the boom is supplied already grooved and glued up, and all that remains for the kit builder to do is to finish it off with some minor shaping and sanding before varnishing. Fig. 44 shows the section of a typical boom with a bolt-rope grooved track. If you are building from drawings you will have ordered your timber to the specification on the drawings. These will probably show two pieces the same size for the boom. You should normally cut these two pieces from the same piece of wood by sawing a square-sectioned length up the centre. The important thing is that the wood must not be glued up again as it was sawn. Examine the wood to see if you can tell from the grain of the two pieces which are the sides that were sawn apart. Lay them together as they were before the wood was sawn, and turn one piece round through 180°. In this way any tendency to bend along either axis will be obviated, after the boom has been glued up again.

145

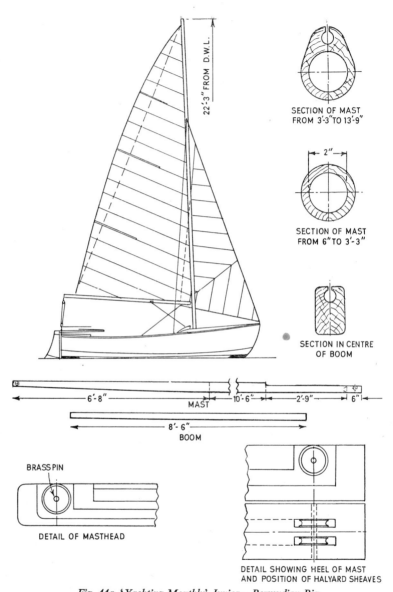

SECTION OF MAST
FROM 3'-3" TO 13'-9"

SECTION OF MAST
FROM 6" TO 3'-3"

SECTION IN CENTRE
OF BOOM

22'-3" FROM D.W.L.

6'-8"

MAST

10'-6"

2'-9"

6"

8'-6"

BOOM

BRASS PIN

DETAIL OF MASTHEAD

DETAIL SHOWING HEEL OF MAST
AND POSITION OF HALYARD SHEAVES

Fig. 44a. 'Yachting Monthly' Junior – Bermudian Rig.

(Courtesy: 'Yachting Monthly')

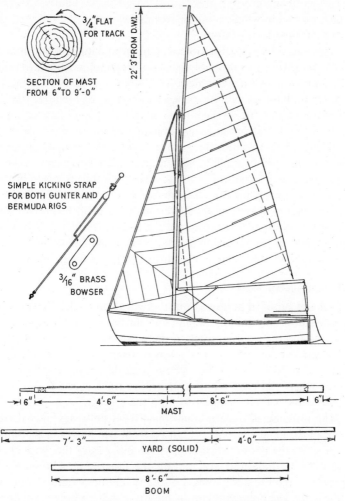

¾" FLAT FOR TRACK

SECTION OF MAST FROM 6" TO 9'-0"

22' 3" FROM D.W.L.

SIMPLE KICKING STRAP FOR BOTH GUNTER AND BERMUDA RIGS

³⁄₁₆" BRASS BOWSER

6"   4'-6"   8'-6"   6"
MAST

7'-3"   4'-0"
YARD (SOLID)

8'-6"
BOOM

Fig. 44b. 'Yachting Monthly' Junior – Gunter Rig.
(Courtesy: 'Yachting Monthly')

Mark on the two inner sides the groove to be cut, and cut it with a grooving plane. You can do this with a mallet and gauge, sanding it afterwards with sandpaper round a piece of dowelling.

The lips of the grooved track must be set back slightly, as indicated on the drawings, to allow free movement of the sail when it is being fitted to the boom.

The main difficulty for the amateur in making the boom and the mast is that you probably have no bench long enough to take the boom and still less the mast. The boom must be flat for gluing up. If you have no suitable bench choose part of the floor that is absolutely flat. Glue up the boom and clamp up one clamp at least every 12 in. If this presents any difficulty use sandbags or weights.

If any glue oozes into the groove, it must be removed at once, as it is almost impossible to shift it after it has hardened. Make a large knot on a length of string so that the knot fits easily in the groove, and draw it through from one end to the other. The glue that remains will be smoothed over on the sides of the groove. All that has to be done now is to shape the boom externally as required and finish off for varnishing. Remember when the varnishing is finished to see that there is no varnish clogging the groove.

The Bermudian Mast

Masts are supplied hollowed out and glued up in the kits so that they require only minor shaping and finishing. The fitting of the sheaves and the external track, if there is to be one, will also have to be carried out. The mast is hollowed from the masthead sheave down to within a foot or two of the heel, depending on the boat. Some masts will have a bolt-rope groove track as the boom, and others a brass track screwed to it on the aft side.

The building of a Bermudian mast from drawings only needs a lot of care and space. It is built up from two halves in the same manner as the boom. Mark out on the inner sides the amount of wood to be hollowed out, noting the taper. Fig. 44a shows a section of the Bermudian mast of the 'Yachting Monthly' Junior. If you find the hollowing out of the mast and the boom too difficult and you cannot obtain them already built up, a joiner's shop with a spindle moulding machine or a router will probably be able to help you. Give them plenty of warning so that they can fit the work in with their production without setting up the machine specially. They will only charge you a few shillings.

Cut out the slots for the sheaves according to the drawing and glue up, but leave in the hollow one length of string for each halyard that will have to be pulled through. Tie each end to a piece of wood so that the strings cannot be pulled through by mistake. Clean out the bolt-rope groove as for the boom. Shaping the outside of the mast need not be a long job if you set about it in the right way. Make up some templates of cardboard; the drawings will show sections of the mast in two or three places. Cut these out in cardboard accurately. Mark the required taper on two opposite sides of the mast, and plane down to the line. Mark the two remaining sides in the same way and plane them likewise. In all probability the bottom two or three feet of the mast will be left square. If you can possibly avoid it, do not clamp on the rounded surfaces or they will be marked for good. Clamp either to a bench or a trestle. If you have got two trestles, keep the second trestle under the area being planed to support it. Be careful not to cut the string for the halyards. It is best to wrap them securely round a small piece of wood and push them down into the sheave slot just below the level to which you are planing. They can be pulled out afterwards and secured to longer pieces of wood again.

As the mast is unlikely to be a true circle in section, no regular procedure can be laid down. The best plan is to plane the edges away a little at a time and keep turning the mast over. It is also important to plane down the whole length of one side before starting on the other.

Finish off with sandpaper on a cork block, but do not rely on the sandpaper to do the work that the plane should do. It may seem easier, but you will lose time and accuracy.

The Gunter Mast

A Gunter mast is a great deal easier than the Bermudian as it is not hollow and generally is truly round. The planing is therefore fairly simple. Plane first to an octagon, then to sixteen sides, and finally round, leaving if necessary a flat down the aft side for an external track. If this is not called for, the mainsail will be laced to the mast. The head of the mast will be probably stepped down slightly to take the spliced eyes of the shroud and forestay.

The Gunter Yard or Gaff

This is used in conjunction with the Gunter mast (see Fig. 44b).
If the yard is solid, the mainsail will be laced to it, but in some
cases it is grooved like the boom. It can be fitted to the mast by
a sliding gooseneck or by gaff jaws (see Fig. 45). If you are

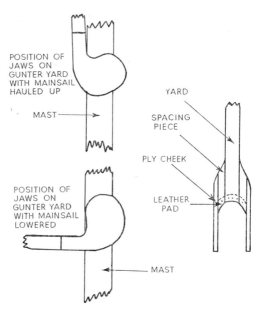

POSITION OF
JAWS ON
GUNTER YARD
WITH MAINSAIL
HAULED UP

MAST

YARD

SPACING
PIECE

PLY CHEEK

POSITION OF
JAWS ON
GUNTER YARD
WITH MAINSAIL
LOWERED

LEATHER
PAD

MAST

Fig. 45. Gaff jaws.

building from drawings the grooved gaff is made in exactly the
same way as the boom. Fitting gaff jaws is quite simple. The foot
of the gaff should be left square after the remainder has been
rounded for a distance of six inches at least. It is easier to shape
most of the gaff before the jaws are fitted. Pack out the two
opposite sides of the foot of the gaff by two spacing pieces. When
fitted the overall width should be between $\frac{1}{8}$ and $\frac{1}{4}$ in more than
the width of the base of the mast, where the mast reaches the deck.
The actual width will depend on whether you are lining the jaws
with leather to protect the mast or not; but there must be enough

clearance for the gaff to run down easily and not jamb. Two ply cheeks should be screwed to the packing pieces (see Fig. 45). These are glued and screwed into position. The shape must allow the gaff to lie horizontal when the mainsail is being lowered, and as near vertical as is required when it is being hauled up. Round and shape the packing pieces to blend with the shape of the gaff. The inside of the jaws can be lined with leather after the gaff has been varnished. The leather should be tacked on with copper nails so placed that they do not come into contact with the mast and defeat the object of the leather.

Mast Sheaves

A sheave (see plate 35) is the grooved wheel that is located in a pulley block. It should run free on the spindle, the rope running in the groove. Sheaves are used independently when they can be housed in some particular component such as the mast where the wood of the mast surrounding the sheave takes the place of the cheeks of the block. The sheave let into the masthead takes the place of a block secured to the masthead and avoids a lot of trouble. Fig. 46 shows the boxed sheave – by far the best type to fit. The danger with sheaves is their tendency to wear down the surrounding wood. There is also the chance that the constant downward pull of the halyard will make the spindle of the sheave sink slightly. If the spindle is located in a soft piece of grain in a silver spruce mast, again the wear of the wood by the sheave will be increased, and eventually the halyard will jump off the sheave and jamb, sometimes with disastrous results. The mast has usually to be lowered to free it. This accident is particularly likely to happen when the main halyard is spliced to wire.

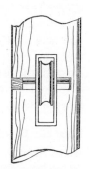

Fig. 46.
Boxed sheave.

(Courtesy: Bell Wood-
working Co. Ltd)

The sides of the boxed sheave are a close fit to the sheave. The sheave and the box are made of Tufnol, which is ideally suited to this type of fitting. It is hard-wearing and light. It does not warp or swell, and it is completely unaffected by the elements.

Open out the slot in the mast for the box so that the box is a press fit in the slot. Bore out the hole for the spindle. Do not bore right through the mast, but leave about $\frac{1}{4}$ in of wood on one side. Push the box and sheave into the slot and drive in the spindle. This spindle is best made of brass rod. Cut it short so that there is still $\frac{1}{4}$ or $\frac{1}{2}$ in of the hole left unfilled after the spindle is driven home. Plug the hole that is left with a piece of dowel. Grease the spindle and keep it greased. There is little likelihood of your having to take it down again. Should you need to do so drill a small hole at the opposite end of the spindle to the plug and drive a nail through it; this will push the plug and spindle out.

As an alternative to the boxed sheave, the slot can be lined along the sides and bottom with a U of brass sheet inserted in the slot; but the boxed sheave is a much better job in every way.

Boxed sheaves are important for the Gunter or Bermudian masts. They are rather more important for the latter because the main halyards are usually spliced to wire, which is more likely to jam between the sheave and the mast, being smaller in diameter than the rope. Apart from the sheave in the masthead the jib halyard will also require a sheave in a Bermudian mast, and probably two sheaves will be required in the base of the mast for both halyards to be brought out into the boat.

Mast and Boom Fittings

All of these will vary from boat to boat; and in some cases from kit to kit, depending on the supplier. There are many different makes of fittings with their own variations. The gooseneck boom fitting is a type commonly used on small dinghies for the boom; it is supplied with a square on the shank. The boom fitting corresponding to it is made from sheet brass (see Fig. 47). The hole in the boom will be square to suit the shank. Screw on the boom fitting and bore the hole to suit the round part of the shank. Chisel out the hole to suit the square on the gooseneck. It is difficult to cut the hole to the correct depth as it is blind. For reefing the boom is withdrawn far enough for the square on the shank of the gooseneck fitting to be clear of the boom fitting, with the round part still in the hole. The boom can then be rotated taking the sail with it for reefing. The aft end of the boom will have a similar fitting except that, instead of a hole bored in the centre, a short brass plate is fitted by a round-headed brass screw into the end of the boom. The main sheet tackle is attached to the plate. When the boom is rotated the plate stays in position, and the screw in the end turns with the boom. So the hole in the plate must be an easy fit on the shank of the screw. At the same time, the screw must be a tight fit in the boom, or it may pull out when under strain.

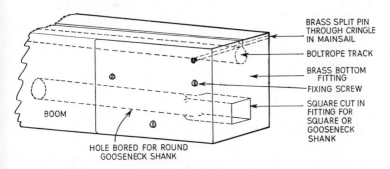

BRASS SPLIT PIN
THROUGH CRINGLE
IN MAINSAIL

BOLTROPE TRACK

BRASS BOTTOM
FITTING

FIXING SCREW

SQUARE CUT IN
FITTING FOR
SQUARE OR
GOOSENECK
SHANK

BOOM

HOLE BORED FOR ROUND
GOOSENECK SHANK

Fig. 47. Boom fitting.

The sliding gooseneck for the boom has the advantage of being adjustable in two ways. Firstly, if there is any adjustment permissible in the height of the mainsail luff, this can be carried out on the slide, and the mainsail can be hoisted higher. Secondly, you can adjust the tension in the luff. Where the mainsail is fitted to the mast by the bolt-rope fitting in the grooved track, the track supplied with the gooseneck will be between 12 and 18 in long; but in some cases the brass track will run up to the masthead, and the sail is fitted to it by small brass slides (see plate 35). Similarly with the Gunter rig the brass track is sometimes run up near the masthead sheave if the Gunter yard is attached by a gooseneck fitting. This fitting consists of a small plate with a slide on the end to run on the track.

Care must be taken to see that the track is screwed down dead straight and that no screw heads are left too high to foul the sail slides. The danger of this type of track is that, if it is dented or damaged in any way the slides will jamb. Take care when trailing the boat that the track is uppermost when stowed in the boat, and that the boom is not hitting the track. If you are buying the track separately you have various kinds to choose from. They fall into two types – the external and the internal. They both fit on the mast in the same way, the difference being that on the internal type the track sides are bent round and the slide fits between them, whereas on the external type the slide fits over the track.

Blocks

To my mind the chief difficulty with all blocks lies in deciphering the written instructions. You will not be bothered with this when ordering a kit, but you may have difficulty in disentangling all the parts. Plate 34 illustrates the main types you will meet. They will usually be supplied in Tufnol with stainless steel, gunmetal, or manganese bronze used for the smaller components such as the eyes, beckets, etc. They are extremely strong and suitable in every way, being non-corrosive and causing the minimum wear on the rigging.

Miscellaneous Fittings

Naturally all the fittings must be made of materials that resist corrosion. Tufnol, apart from being used for blocks and sheaves, is also used for a number of other fittings, such as cleats and fair-leads, and is incorporated into many others as well. Gunmetal, bronze, brass, and galvanized iron are the other most commonly used materials. Recently a new range of fittings made from aluminium alloy have been put on the market by Messrs Jack Holt Ltd. They are marketed under the name of Holt-Allen and offer a wide variety. The advantages of them are that they are light and cheaper than many of the others: at the same time they are robust and look very neat. Plate 31 shows one of the jambing cleats. Fig. 48 shows how to make a 6-in wooden cleat from ash.

Fig. 49 shows the sheet horse and, on the same drawing, an alternative tackle that can be used for the main sheet with

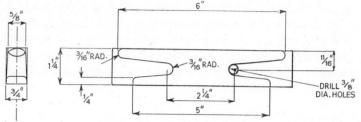

Fig. 48. Shaping a 6-in wooden cleat.

eye-bolts in the deck instead of the horse. This tackle can be used with advantage if an outboard bracket would interfere with the horse. This is not the sort of modification you should make in a class boat without consulting the class rules.

The last item of importance is the stem plate. The details vary a lot and are hardly relevant. The object of the plate is to secure to the stem of the boat the forestay, the jib and the spinnaker, if you have one. It is usually a triangular plate which lies flat on the bow with a short length projecting from the underside down the stem, the whole being firmly screwed down. On top is a small fin with two or three holes in it. If there are three holes, the centre hole is for securing the forestay, the aft hole is for the tack of the jib, and the forward hole is for the tack of the spinnaker.

In plate 35 a simple type of chain plate is shown. Chain plates can vary considerably in design. Their object is to secure the

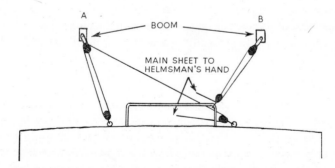

Fig. 49. Sheet horse and alternative method using blocks, looking at the stern.

bottom end of the shrouds to the hull, and it is better that they should be secured with bolts rather than screws. Some types are adjustable, which is an advantage as any stretching in the standing rigging can be taken up by the chain plates as well as by the rigging screw on the forestay. Plate 35 shows a typical rigging screw. These screws should be kept greased.

Stem Band

A stem band is usually supplied in the kits. If it is not supplied, it is well worth buying as an extra. It is a brass strip, half round in section, screwed on the stem, starting where the stem plate ends, and continuing right down the stem and along the keel to the transom. It is particularly important as it protects the stem and keel from damage. An obstacle arises at the centre-board slot: one way of fitting the band is to take it to the end of the slot and then continue it again at the other end and fit a short length at each side. This procedure does not, however, overcome the danger of the ends being caught on an obstacle and pulling out the fixing screws. The Bell Woodworking Co. offer a special Y fitting to overcome this snag (see plate 32). If, on the other hand, you have a wide keel, the band down the centre will still leave the edges of the keel exposed to damage. If the boat is liable to rough usage, e.g. a pram lying on a stony beach, the edges of the keel will soon become badly worn. I have found that if you fit the banding along each side of the keel for the full length and join it at the base of the stem to a single piece so that it can run up the stem, the keel is protected; but if there is a dagger-plate as in the pram or a centre-plate, the edges of the slot will become worn; this is the lesser of two evils.

Rowlocks

I think that the beginner must have oars for family sailing. The rowlocks should be fitted roughly 12 in aft of the thwart which the oarsman is using. If the boat has no side decking, you will probably have to thicken the gunwales at the point where the rowlocks are fitted. To do this, glue and screw a length of wood 6 in long on each gunwale. The shank of the rowlock should pass through a further block of wood below the gunwale for additional support and for reduction of the strain on the gunwale. The end of the shank should have a small hole in it, about ⅜ in in diameter. When the rowlocks are in position for rowing, tie a short length of cord through this hole, the other end being secured to the boat. It is very easy for a rowlock to jump out into the water if you make a bad shot with an oar. If the cord is long enough, you can pull the rowlock up through the hole and leave the rowlock hanging inboard, handy for dropping into position when the need arises. A word of warning – do not leave rowlocks in the boat unattended.

Rudders

Most kits, other than kits for prams, will provide drop rudders. The drop rudder has the great advantage of allowing the boat to be launched with the rudder shipped. You can then lower the rudder as soon as the water becomes deep enough. If the boat should run aground, the centre-board and the rudder can be raised to allow the boat to float off. The rudders will be partially built up in the kits. There are two types of drop rudder – those that are fitted with a wooden blade (the majority) and those that are fitted with a metal blade. The wooden blade is usually made of ply (see Fig. 50). Being buoyant it floats up and is pulled down with an elastic cord. Some kits provide Kautex friction pads for wooden blades. Kautex, being a synthetic and not a natural rubber, is oil- and grease-resisting, and has superior lasting qualities compared with natural rubber in the face of ozone and sunlight.

In the case of a metal blade the metal's weight will keep the blade down and a length of cord is used to pull the blade up. Assembly of the rudder is quite straightforward. If you are working from drawings you only have to shape the cheeks, stock, and blade. Then you must make the tiller and the tiller extension, if there is to be one. The tiller should be tapered to fit in the tiller hood. Allow a little slack for the varnish and for the swelling of the wood before drilling for the split pin. If you are using an outboard motor, you may find that the tiller is too long. If you do not want to use an extension on the motor itself, you can easily make another, shorter, tiller.

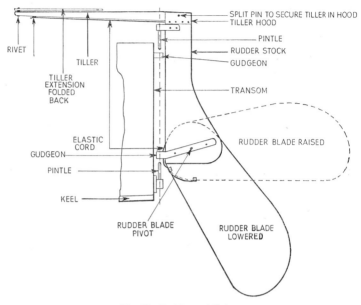

Fig. 50. Rudder and fittings.

I am not normally in favour of gadgets, but there are exceptions. Here is a suggestion. Secure a length of catapult elastic to the hog or frame member under the tiller. Pull the elastic up vertical and, where it touches the tiller, screw an eye. Tie a small hook on the end of the elastic and stretch the elastic when the hook is in the eye on the tiller. This gadget will stop the rudder from swinging about if you have to leave the tiller to attend to something that has gone wrong in another part of the boat and requires two hands to set it right.

XIV

ENGINES, TRAILERS, SAILS, ETC.

Outboard Motors

In recent years an increasing number of first-class trouble-free outboard motors have been developed to suit all classes of boat. The two motor-boats described in this book can both be powered by outboard motors. The 13-ft Runabout is primarily designed for outboard running, and the Bell Basic Hull can be supplied with a recessed transom specially designed for outboard mounting.

Mounting outboard motors on dinghies without any aft decking is easy as the motors are fitted with screw clamps for clamping directly on to the transom. Partially decked boats do present some difficulties. I do not like the idea of cutting a hole in the aft decking to allow the motor to be clamped to the transom. This hole is usually covered by a hatch when the motor is not being used. I think that these hatches spoil the look of the boat. The British Seagull Co. offer two sizes of external mounting bracket suitable for all their motors. These can be bolted directly to the transom without interfering with the deck. It is a very neat arrangement but will not suit all types of boat. Fig. 51 shows one of the two external brackets for the Seagull range of outboards.

The British Anzani Co. Ltd offer some very useful suggestions, as illustrated in Fig. 52. With the help of these methods you should be able to avoid spoiling your decking. Whatever type of bracket you choose you must attach it to the boat with bolts and not with screws. There is bound to be vibration and bolts are far more secure. Under the nut on the bolt it is important to fit a shake-proof washer, or better still fit a lock nut. You will look pretty silly if the bracket should work loose and you drop the whole assembly into the water. Dropping outboards overboard is not an insurable risk and is expressly excluded from insurance policies. Frequently, when our boat is lying at moorings, I have had to row out in a pram, taking the outboard with me. Fixing it in position in a swell is quite a delicate operation. As a safety

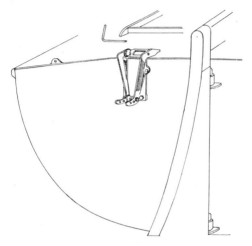

Bronze 'bolt-on' bracket for decked boats enables motor to be dropped into position in a few seconds.

1. If possible mount bracket on port side of centre line.

2. Adjust thrust-block if necessary to bring motor in a vertical position when driving boat.

Fig. 51. Seagull auxiliary mounting for small sailing craft.
Type '40' Seagull patented 'Bolt-on' bracket.
(*Courtesy: The British Seagull Co. Ltd, Poole, Dorset*)

precaution on these occasions I tie a length of cod line to the outboard and on the other end a cork float. If the outboard should be dropped in the water, the cork will float and the motor can be hauled up again with relative ease.

I prefer an outboard of proven design with as few gadgets as possible. Read the instructions carefully and look after the handbook. Both the makes I have mentioned are supplied with very thorough and lucid instructions. By and large, failure to start or bad starting is the fault of the owner more often than of the motor; so make yourself familiar with your engine before you attach it to the boat.

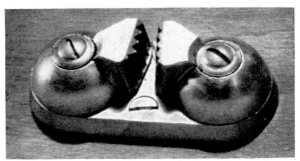

31. Holt-Allen alloy jambing cleat

*32. Bell Woodworking Y fitting to take the keel band round the
centre-board slot*

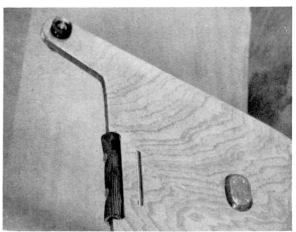

*33. A friction method of maintaining and adjusting a wooden
centre-board in any desired position. The screws in the hose are
tightened until the correct amount of tension is obtained*

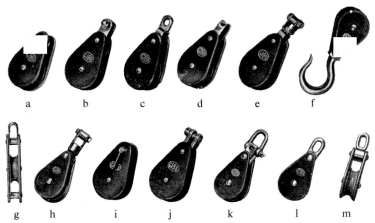

34. A selection of blocks and various fittings, for dinghies and small yachts

(a) bow; (b) fork and pin across; (c) swivel eye; (d) fixed eye; (e) swivel shackle; (f) hook;
(g) fixed eye and becket in line; (h) swivel shackle; (i) drop nose pin; (j) fork and pin in line;
(k) reversible shackle; (l) oval eye in line; (m) oval eye across

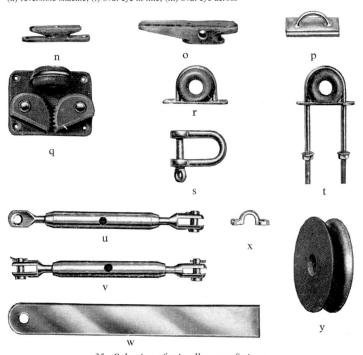

35. Selection of miscellaneous fittings

(n) Tufnol dinghy cleat—jambs with one turn; (o) Tufnol jambing cleat; (p) eyeslide for track;
(q) Tufnol cam jambing cleat with bullseye lead; (r) screw down bullseye lead; (s) D shackle;
(t) bolt through bullseye lead; (u) rigging screw (bottlescrew) fork and eye; (v) rigging screw
(bottlescrew) fork and fork; (w) chain plate; (x) inside eye; (y) Tufnol sheave

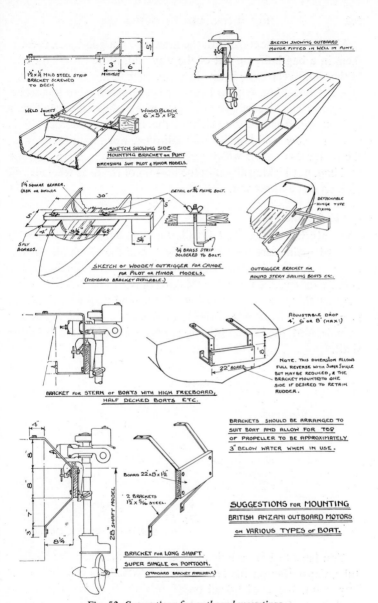

Fig. 52. Suggestions for outboard mountings.

(Courtesy: British Anzani Engineering Co. Ltd)

Always keep the tools with the motor. It is a good plan to keep them in a bag hung up out of the way and, more important, out of the wet. I keep mine in an old gas-mask bag hanging on a hook under the decking. A petrol can for spare petrol is an important accessory. The ideal can is a one-gallon can supplied by Halford's cycle shops. It is half the height of the usual two-gallon can, it is easier to stow, and less likely to fall over. For filling the tank of the motor use a filler which screws on to the can. Keep it in the tool bag, not kicking about in the bottom of the boat where it will pick up dirt and get wet.

Power Installations

The only boats described in this book that can be fitted with inboard engines are the Bell Basic Hull and the 'Yachting World' Runabout. There is a wide range of excellent marine engines made in this country, and if you are thinking of fitting an inboard engine the first thing to do is to consult the engine manufacturers and give them all the details of the boat. When the type of engine has been decided, the keel and the hog must be bored for the propeller shaft.

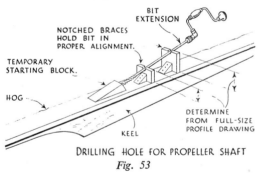

DRILLING HOLE FOR PROPELLER SHAFT

Fig. 53

(*Courtesy: Bell Woodworking Co. Ltd*)

You have to bore a hole at an angle for the propeller shaft or tube, depending on the arrangement adopted. This hole is most important. It must be dead true fore and aft and at the correct angle to the hog. You can only find the correct angle when the exact position of the engine has been determined.

The angle to be bored must be carefully laid off and a temporary jig must be rigged up on the hog (see Fig. 53). A pilot hole is first bored with an auger or an extension bit and brace. The pilot hole is then opened out to the required size for the tube or shaft. A boring bar must be begged or borrowed. This is the best and most reliable method of boring the hole to the correct size. There are other ways such as burning out, but I do not think that this should

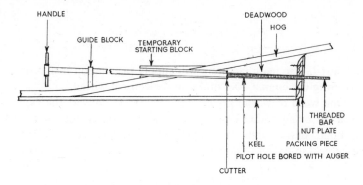

Fig. 54. Operation of boring bar.

be attempted by a beginner. The boring bar may be difficult to get hold of, and if you cannot find one you must have the hole bored for you; in fact, if you are in any doubt about your ability to carry out the operation, you should have it done professionally. Fig. 54 shows the function of a boring bar.

If a stern tube is used it must be a good fit in the hole to prevent leakage. The inboard end of the shaft will be located in a bearing, and the engine will be coupled to the shaft by a flexible coupling. Stuart Turner, who are well-known manufacturers of small marine engines, offer an adjustable metal shaft log which simplifies the whole procedure of fitting the propeller shaft (see Fig. 55). You can see the log in position on the deadwood, together with the shaft in the log and running in an 'A' bracket. This arrangement is ideal for small cruisers and runabouts. The adjustable log allows a small margin of error in boring the hole, the bearing being finally locked in position after correct alignment has been

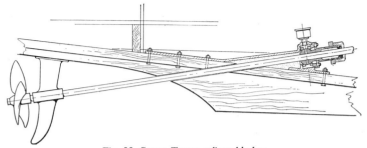

Fig. 55. Stuart Turner adjustable log.
(*Courtesy: Bell Woodworking Co. Ltd*)

achieved. The manufacturers will supply installation instructions covering the engine, fuel tanks, and electrical wiring.

One word of warning – do not attempt to convert the engine of a car or any other type of petrol or paraffin engine for use in a boat, unless you have considerable experience of internal combustion engines in general and marine engines in particular.

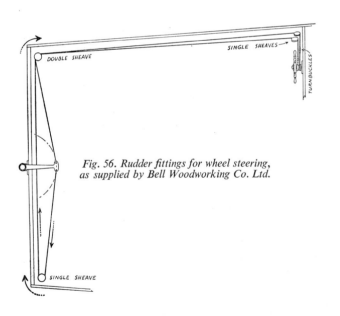

Fig. 56. Rudder fittings for wheel steering, as supplied by Bell Woodworking Co. Ltd.

Rudder Mechanisms on Power Boats

Steering small boats fitted with outboard motors presents no problems. The motors swivel on their mountings. An extension can be fitted to the existing tiller arm if required, so the rudder of the boat need not be used unless you particularly want it.

The situation on larger boats with inboard engines is rather different. It is important to purchase a really reliable rudder gear.

Fig. 56 illustrates a layout using parts supplied by the Bell Woodworking Co. The steering is carried from the tiller arm by flexible cables working in boxed sheaves, the shells of which are so designed that any angle of entry and exit can be arranged. The whole system can be adjusted to suit special requirements.

Fend-offs

For normal sailing-dinghies fend-offs are not an indispensable item of equipment, but for a knock-about dinghy in which you potter about with an outboard motor they are a great help.

They are expensive to buy but easy to make. It is no use making them with a covering material that is rough and abrasive as it will only rub paint off the boat. A fend-off made of woven or plaited rope is ideal for a tug, but will soon wear away the paint on a dinghy hull.

Canvas makes a suitable covering. Sew it in the form of a sausage to a suitable length. The best filling is foam rubber, which can be bought from second-hand dealers in odd pieces fairly cheap. The ideal size is slabs 1 in thick, which you cut into strips, the width of each strip equalling the length of the covering bag. Cut the strips with a bread knife, wetting the knife with water so that it does not stick to the rubber. Roll the strips up and push them into the bag. Sew up the end, leaving a flap or tongue for the brass eyelet. These eyelets can be ticklish to fit without the right tool. They are supplied in two halves and should be punched together either side of the canvas with a punch and die made to suit each particular size of eyelet; but you can manage without a punch and die.

Bore a hole in a piece of wood the same size as the hole in the eyelet. Cut a hole in the canvas to take the larger half of the eyelet.

Push this through the canvas hole and place the other half in the shape of a washer over the rim protruding through the canvas. Clamp the piece of wood in the vice and put the eyelet over it so that the two holes correspond. You will require a piece of metal which is tapered to make the point go through the hole; a screw-driver may do or even the point of a pick-axe. Work it round so that the rim of the eyelet splays out over the washer, then hammer it flat against the washer. Splice a length of line through the eyelet for securing to the boat.

Granulated cork as used for packing fruit can be used for filling; it can be obtained for nothing from most greengrocers. The snag about it is that it holds water and soon rots the canvas if it is left waterlogged. You leave a trail of cork behind you, and the bag is soon empty. Another dodge is to wind a length of rope round and push it into the bag.

Sails and Rigging

Forms of rigging vary considerably in detail, but they should present no problems as they are supplied either in kits or as an extra. Alternatively, you can purchase direct from a sailmaker. If you do this, be sure to give full details to the sailmaker and do not leave your purchase till the last moment. In the spring and early summer there is always a rush to order sails and deliveries are apt to be delayed.

If you want to pursue 'Do it Yourself' to the very end, you can make all the sails and rigging yourself. It is outside the scope of this book to tell you how to do this. An excellent book on the subject by Bowker and Budd has recently been published by Macmillan. It covers the whole subject of sailmaking very thoroughly. Bowker and Budd also supply all the necessary materials for any set of sails if you tell them what you require. Even if you feel you cannot face making the sails yourself, you will find in this book useful details on maintenance, splicing, and rope work.

New rigging and sails need careful handling if they are to serve you well. The spliced eyes will stretch on the wire rope used for the standing rigging, i.e. the forestay and shrouds. If they appear short when you first rig the boat, you can always insert a shackle between the rigging screw on the stem plate and the bottom of the forestay. This can be taken out afterwards when the rigging has stretched.

The sails must be carefully and evenly stretched. Choose a dry, calm day with a light breeze and set off under full sail. The foresail luff should be stretched tight in the normal way as the luff wire will not alter in length; it is already cut to the correct size by the maker. The mainsail requires greater care.

Where practicable, rig the boat on dry land first to get the hang of it. Draw the foot rope into the groove or track on the boom. The tack will probably be secured by a large brass split pin to the boom. Draw the clew out until it is finger-tight and secure it to the end of the boom. Enter the luff of the mainsail in the groove or track on the mast, hoist the mainsail finger-tight and secure the main halyard. Make sure that there are no local strains on the foot ropes or the luff. Do not try to pull out any wrinkles in the canvas as these will shake out on their own.

For the first sail drive the boat gently. Do not try to pin her in hard or drive her hard to windward. Quite soon the luff of the mainsail and to a lesser degree the foot rope will become slack, and the wrinkles in the canvas will soon disappear. Keep the sails dry and do not reef them until they are fully stretched; in fact, if a reef is needed, you have no business to be out with new sails.

Kicking Strap

The kicking strap is a length of line secured near the base of the mast running out at approximately 45° up to the boom. It should be adjustable and its object is to prevent the boom kicking or rising up, especially when the mainsheet is freed. It should be easily detachable from the boom and will not be required when sailing close-hauled, as the mainsheet will serve the same purpose.

Toe Straps

These are webbing straps fitted alongside the centre-board case, one on each side, in order that the crew may lean over the gunwale gaining support for their toes under the straps.

Buoyancy

A boat by virtue of its design floats in water and is therefore buoyant, and a wooden boat will float even when capsized and full of water, though only the top of the gunwales may show above water. All metal parts and paint, etc., will reduce the buoyancy of the craft.

I believe it to be imperative to fit additional buoyancy in all small sailing boats, except possibly in sailing prams. The question then arises of how much buoyancy should be added. Although a dinghy will float when swamped, it should have additional buoyancy sufficient to keep the boat as high up in the water as possible, and also to support the crew in their waterlogged clothes. As a rough estimate the buoyancy should be at least equal to the dead weight of the boat, and preferably more, to make it easier to right it. With luck the boat can be bailed out, but this depends on the boat and how the buoyancy is fitted.

Buoyancy falls into two classes – the built-in variety and the additional buoyancy fitted in the form of bags or tanks. Some boats, such as the Graduate and the Osprey, have water-tight compartments under the fore and aft decking and under the side decking, on each side of the cockpit. Built-in buoyancy has the advantage that it is ready-made for you, and on the whole it is more effective because the greater area is sealed off.

Buoyancy can be added to a boat by inflated rubberized canvas or plastic bags, metal cans, or drums. Buoyancy bags are probably the most popular form of additional buoyancy, but are a bit of a nuisance as they have to be blown up and are liable to puncture. The best ones are rubberized canvas and the cheapest are plastic. As they are a difficult shape and are really balloons, they take up a lot of space for the buoyancy they give and cannot be fitted in odd corners.

Oil drums or cans may be used. They are very unsightly and take up space, but they are cheap. They must be watched for rust.

The Baxenden Chemical Co. Ltd have produced a plastic material known as Spandoplast. It is relatively new on the market and has a number of advantages. It is a cellular plastic material with excellent characteristics as solid buoyancy; it is strong, light, and tough-skinned. It should be painted before being fitted into the boat. It is supplied in thicknesses up to 4 in in slabs 3 by 1 ft and 3 by 2 ft. It can be sawn or glued owing to its chemical nature. It is important that only glues and paints recommended by the manufacturers should be used. Spandoplast has a density of 2 lb per cu ft. The following table may be useful for calculating buoyancy.

One 5-gallon oil drum will give 50 lb of buoyancy, less the weight of the drum (approx. 5 lb).

1 cu ft of water weighs 63 lb.

1 cu ft of Spandoplast painted gives 60 lb of buoyancy.

1 buoyancy bag 4 ft 6 in × 10 in equals $2\frac{1}{2}$ cu ft or 158 lb of buoyancy less the weight of the bag.

On my present boat I am fitting 6 cu ft of Spandoplast in slabs 4 in thick, giving over 360 lb of buoyancy at a cost of about £3 10s, whereas the equivalent in top-quality bags would cost between £5 and £6. One can fit the slabs with webbing straps well out of the way, under the side decking and under the aft and fore decking. When fitting bags or Spandoplast as buoyancy, you should fit them against the gunwales and not at the bottom of the boat. You have to compromise up to a point. If the top of the centre-board is some distance below the gunwales and you capsize, you may not be able to bail out faster than the water comes in at the top of the centre-board case; but if you put the buoyancy too low, the boat will float all right, but upside down, and you will have considerable difficulty in righting her on your own.

Finally, make quite sure that whatever type of buoyancy you add to your boat is secured properly. Otherwise it will pop out when you capsize and float gently away.

Trailers

I have very definite views on home-made trailers. A lot of people seem to lose interest when it comes to the trailer. Every summer one sees a number of 'lash-ups' which have no business to be on the road at all.

To make a good reliable trailer is not so easy as it looks, as

I know to my cost. If you have made a good job of a boat worth say £150, it is a pity to risk its life on an unsound trailer. There are several makes on the market. They may seem expensive, but they are soundly designed and constructed with the right materials.

If you are going to make your own trailer, there are a number of methods and a variety of materials one can use. Here are some important facts to be remembered:

(*a*) THE LAW

Perhaps the most important consideration of all. Trailers for the majority of trailable boats are under 2 cwt unladen weight, and therefore are not required to have brakes of any sort. I have never understood this ruling. You can load the trailer as much as you like and need have no brakes, provided that the trailer complies with the unladen weight limit.

For large motor cruisers and some sailing craft it will be necessary to have a larger trailer. If the unladen weight is between 2 cwt and 1 ton, brakes acting automatically on the overrun are sufficient to comply with the regulations, but the unladen weight must be clearly marked on the near side of the trailer.

The width must not exceed 7 ft 6 in and the length must not exceed 22 ft, excluding the draw-bar. No additional tax has to be paid for a trailer drawn by a privately licensed vehicle. The insurance policy of the car should provide for indemnity against third-party risks, as required by law. An existing policy can usually be endorsed to this effect.

A speed limit of 30 m.p.h. is imposed on two-wheel trailers towed by cars, provided both the car and the trailer have pneumatic tyres; otherwise the limit is 20 m.p.h. This limit applies everywhere. It cost me 2 guineas and an endorsement to exceed it one year.

A number-plate with the towing vehicle's index mark must be displayed at the rear of the towed vehicle and illuminated when on the road after lighting-up time. 'T' (trailer) plates are not essential for trailers drawn by private cars.

If you are travelling on a long journey, you should note that a vehicle must not be left for an unreasonable time on the highway.

The roadside verge often forms part of the highway. Lay-bys have been made on many roads for temporary stops, but in general they may not be used for overnight parking. It is illegal to light a fire on the highway or within 50 ft of it.

(b) LIGHTS

For the sake of convenience the number-plates are usually fitted on a strip of metal with the lights and reflectors fitted to it. The whole contraption is fitted to the stern of the boat for towing. The

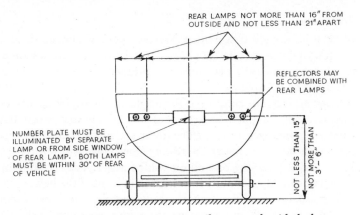

Fig. 57. Lighting arrangements on a trailer to comply with the law.

bar or strip can be fixed to the upper rudder gudgeon, and a length of cord from each end taken to a cleat on the aft deck or to the sheet horse will keep it secure. The only snag arises if you want to tow the trailer at night without the boat. If the bar is fitted to the trailer it may be below the limit for the lights (see Fig. 57).

(c) NOTES ON TRAILER DESIGN

A number of different materials can be used – wood, mild steel tubing, angle iron, channel or T section being the most easily obtainable and most suitable. Non-ferrous alloys in the same form can be used, but be sure they are of adequate strength.

The most usual designs in plan are those of an equilateral triangle or T shape, the axle being located on the base of the triangle or the top of the T. There is no need for the frame to extend aft of the wheels more than is necessary for fitting the springs.

The best way to carry the boat is bow first with the weight distributed so that there is no more than ½-cwt downward thrust on the coupling to the car. Under no circumstances must the trailer be loaded so that she is stern heavy. It will ride very badly and slide on the corners, causing undue wear on the coupling and tyres and spring bushes.

The Frame

Mild steel tubing is best welded. Many garages will undertake the job for you at a reasonable charge. It is better to have a lighter gauge section of tube and build box-girder fashion than have a heavier tube unsupported.

Your aim should be to keep the height of the trailer as low as possible, but see that the keel does not hit the axle when the trailer is going over a bump. The lower the whole structure complete with boat, the better the towing; the trailer will not roll as much and the loading on and off will be easier. The coupling or draw-bar should be about 1 ft to 1 ft 6 in in front of the bow.

The usual method for supporting the boat is to have two foam rubber supports aft, one each side. If possible, one support should be under a chine or frame and one forward within 3–4 ft of the bow. These supports should be 3 in wide at least and 10–12 in long. It is quite simple to stick foam rubber to wood with Bostik and cover the rubber with canvas.

A support for a Bermudian mast can easily be fitted behind the coupling. It is also helpful to fit a short bar behind the coupling, about 2 ft long at right angles to the trailer as a lifting handle. Two bicycle handle-bar grips can be fitted, one each end.

Wheels and Springs

At an early stage you must start thinking about buying components such as wheels and springs. Suitable parts can sometimes be found in car breakers' yards or old aircraft dumps. If cost is not supremely important, get new parts from the outset. If you are prepared to spend a lot of time and money searching dumps, you may get what you want, but you will be extremely lucky if you pick up what you want in the way of springs. Half-elliptical springs from an old Baby Austin are adequate, but they are difficult to fit and are going to make the trailer higher. The correct springs cost from 20s to 30s each. They do not need shackles, whereas old car springs often do. One transverse elliptical spring can be used, but it is not easy to fit and makes the boat higher off the ground.

One method is to take a rigid axle and use one spring at each end. This is a cheap way, but you must see that the axle is strong enough not to flare when the wheels splay out under strain. This tendency is directly related to loaded weight and length of axle.

The second method is to have two short axles, each with a quarter-elliptical spring on each side of the wheel. This gives independent suspension and the chance to get the boat nearer the ground without fouling the axle, but the cost will be higher because of the double number of springs. The saving in the amount of metal will be offset by the amount of machining required on the two short axles.

Wheels

It pays every time to buy the right kind of wheels; they should always be pneumatic. Motor-cycle wheels are too big unless they are supplied with a complicated suspension system. One can occasionally find wheels at an aircraft dump, but most of them are unsuitable.

There are a number of suppliers advertising in motoring and yachting journals who offer a range of wheels. Their lists are likely to show the maximum load for each wheel. To ensure maximum safety, this should be three times the total weight of the trailer for two wheels. A wheel with a maximum load capacity of 750 lb gives 1,500 lb for two wheels, allowing a safe total weight for the trailer and load of 500 lb. This allows for shock loads which are difficult to calculate, but occur whenever you hit a bump.

If you pick up wheels from a dump, make sure that replacement tyres and tubes are available at a reasonable price. Many old aircraft wheels are obsolete, with new tyres hard to get and dear.

We use our trailer for launching the boat. If you do this, remember to keep the wheel bearings well covered in waterproof grease.

I strongly advise anyone thinking of building a trailer to visit or write to Crevald's Services, who are stockists of all the components.

Couplings

It is important to fit a universal coupling of some kind. A ball-and-socket coupling is the best kind but rather expensive. There are other kinds which are quite suitable. Do not use a bolt through an eye as it will jump out.

Towing

It is difficult to be dogmatic about the maximum loads that can be towed by a car. There are so many factors to be considered and the majority of boats are not heavy enough to constitute a problem. A car with a four-speed gear-box has the advantage over one with a three-speed box. The trailer tyres must be kept at the pressure recommended by the manufacturer.

As a rough guide, the maximum load should not exceed $1\frac{1}{4}$ cwt of load to a unit of h.p. R.A.C. rating.

GLOSSARY

BEAM: Width of a boat.

BEVEL: Edge of a plank, flat but not cut at right angles to the sides (see Fig. 39).

BILGE: The bottom of the boat, inside and out—literally the 'Bulge' (and the water that collects in it). A bilge keel is a small keel on each side of the main keel, usually, in a dinghy to protect the bilge planking.

BOLT-ROPE: Rope sewn along the edge of a sail.

BOOM: Spar, hingeing on the mast, to which foot of mainsail is attached.

BUTT: The squared-off end of a piece of timber. When planks or timbers are 'butted' or 'butt-jointed' they are end to end or edge to edge and often supported by a backing piece (see Fig. 35).

CENTRE-BOARD: A drop keel in the form of a board housed in a case on the hog, hingeing on a pivot which can be raised or lowered usually by means of tackle; the main purpose being to increase the lateral area of the hull and prevent the boat making leeway.

CENTRE-PLATE: As above; this term is generally used when it is made of metal.

CHINE: This is in effect a stringer but is referred to as a chine when it is situated at a change of angle of the boat's side. Where this change is an angle, instead of a continuous curve, the hull is called 'hard chined', or 'double chined' with two angles (see Fig. 59).

CLEAT: A fitting made of wood, metal, or plastic for securing any kind of running rigging or tackle, by winding the rope round the arms of the cleat. A jambing cleat secures a rope without the necessity of taking turns round it (generally not secure unless under tension). It has the advantage of quick release; there are many different types of jambing cleat (see plate 35).

CLEW: The after lower corner of a sail, to which the sheet is attached.

COUNTERSINK: To insert a screw in such a way (by means of an additional recess at the top of the screw hole) that its head is flush with the surface, or lower if needed (see Fig. 38).

CRINGLE: A loop of rope fitted to the edge of a sail through sewn eyelets and carrying a thimble.

DAGGER-PLATE: A wooden, sometimes metal, centre-board which is not pivoted but pushed up and down vertically and lifted inboard when not in use.

FAIRLEAD: A metal or plastic fitting fitted on the deck or gunwales through which pass mooring lines and anchor ropes, etc.: to prevent them wearing the woodwork.

FORESTAY: Wire rope running from the stem to about three-quarters way up the mast, acting as its forward support.

FREEBOARD: General term for that part of the hull side which is above the water level.

FUTTOCKS: Vertical structural timbers, e.g. side members of frames.

GARBOARD or GARBOARD STRAKE: The bottom plank or panel, on either side of the keel; the garboard joint being between this plank and the keel.

GUNWALE: The upper edge of a boat's side.

HALYARD: Rope for hauling up a sail. Attached to the head of a jib or staysail or Bermudian mainsail.

HEAD: The topmost corner of a sail.

HEADSAIL: General term for sails forward of the mast, jibs, staysails, etc.

HOG: Main fore and aft structural timber in a boat at the bottom of the hull (see Fig. 59).

JIB: All boats carrying a headsail in this book, have only one, usually called a jib. It is sometimes called a staysail.

KEEL: The bottom longitudinal piece of timber running the length of the hull; frequently additional keels of wood or metal are added below (false keel).

KICKING STRAP: Tackle, one end of which is attached to the mast near the foot, and the other a short way along the boom, the object being to prevent the end of the boom kicking up when the ship is running before the wind and thus to keep the sail flat.

KNEE: A block of wood cut to support an angled joint, e.g. stem to hog, transom and stern, gunwale and transom.

LAP JOINT: A joint made by the edge of one piece of timber being laid on the side of another.

LEECH: The after edge of a sail.

LEEWARD: The side away from the wind; down wind.

LEEWAY: Sideways drift to leeward caused by wind.

LOOSE-FOOTED: Term applied to a mainsail when the foot is not attached to a spar along its entire length, but only at each extremity. Sometimes a mainsail with no boom.

LUFF: The forward or leading edge of a sail.

MAST GATE: When a dinghy is decked in from the stem as far as the mast, the aft edge of the deck is recessed to take the mast, which is held in by a wooden or metal fitting called a mast gate, the mast being stepped on the hog.

MAST STEP: Block of wood shaped to receive the foot of the mast (usually a square hole). The fitting is either screwed to the hog or keelson, or the fore deck.

PEAK: The topmost corner of the sail.

REEF: To reduce the sail area either by rolling the boom round and wrapping the sail round with it, or by tying the sail down to the boom by means of a row of reef points placed along the sail parallel to the foot.

RETRACTABLE KEEL: A keel which is withdrawn up into the trunking in the hull (see Seagull, page 83).

RIGGING SCREW. Metal device which can be inserted at base of a wire stay and can be used to adjust tension, by screwing or unscrewing.

SAIL BATTEN: Strip of wood or plastic, usually three in number, inserted at right angles into the leech of the mainsail to keep it flat.

SCARF: An extreme form of bevel; for a scarf joint the scarfed surfaces are joined together (see Fig. 34).

SHACKLE: Metal fitting used for connecting rigging to the deck, mast or any fastening.

SHEER: The curve of the gunwale as seen in profile.

SHEET: A rope attached to the clew of the sail for adjusting the set.

SHROUDS: Wire ropes running from the deck or gunwale on either side aft of the mast up to the masthead; on some boats they do not run to the mast head, but about three-quarters way up.

STAY: Wire support for the mast, attached to gunwale and to metal fitting near the top of the mast. Some dinghies only have a forestay (q.v.), others have one on either side of the mast, easily adjustable in length, with a rigging screw or lanyard at the bottom.

STAYSAIL: A headsail whose leading edge clips on to the forestay.

STEM: The essential part of the structure of the bow, a piece of timber running from the hog to the gunwale. In most dinghies in this book it is vertical.

STEM PLATE: A metal plate fitted at the stem to which the forestay and headsails are secured.

STRAKE: Plank or panel (garboard strake *see* garboard). The sheer strake is the top panel or plank, the rubbing strake is an additional plank fitted along the gunwale for protection.

STRINGER: Fore and aft longitudinal structural timbers between gunwale and the hog (see Fig. 59).

TABERNACLE: In cases where the mast is stepped on the deck, it is sometimes housed in a tabernacle, which comprises two cheeks, one each side of the mast foot, with a metal pin passing right through the cheeks and mast, allowing the mast to be lowered, as on a hinge, but still secured inboard.

THIMBLE: A round or heart-shaped metal fitting designed to fit tightly in eyesplices and cringles.

THWART: Wooden plank running across the ship from side to side; used as a seat, e.g. when rowing.

TRANSOM: Flat cut-off stern, formed of a plank or planks at right angles to the centre-line of the boat, usually vertical (see Fig. 59).

TUMBLEHOME: The name given to the curve of a ship's side, when it turns slightly inwards at the gunwale.

WINDWARD: The side the wind is coming from.

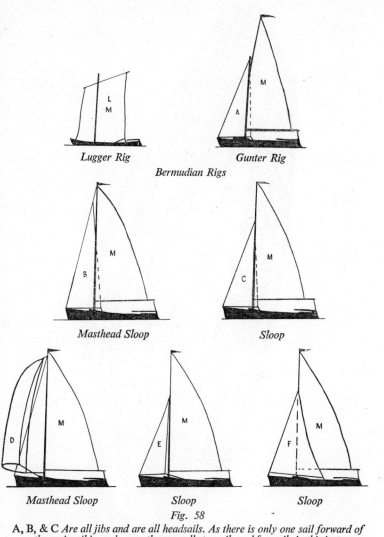

Lugger Rig

Gunter Rig

Bermudian Rigs

Masthead Sloop

Sloop

Masthead Sloop

Sloop

Sloop

Fig. 58

A, B, & C *Are all jibs and are all headsails. As there is only one sail forward of
the mainsail in each case, they are all staysails and foresails in this instance.*

E *This is a storm jib and is appreciably smaller than a normal jib, otherwise
similar in all respects to A, B, and C.*

D *Spinnaker, a light-weight voluminous headsail designed for use in a following
wind, boomed out on the weather side.*

F *Genoa, a long-footed headsail; in these cases also a staysail and foresail.*

L *Lugsail, also called the mainsail.*   M *Mainsail.*

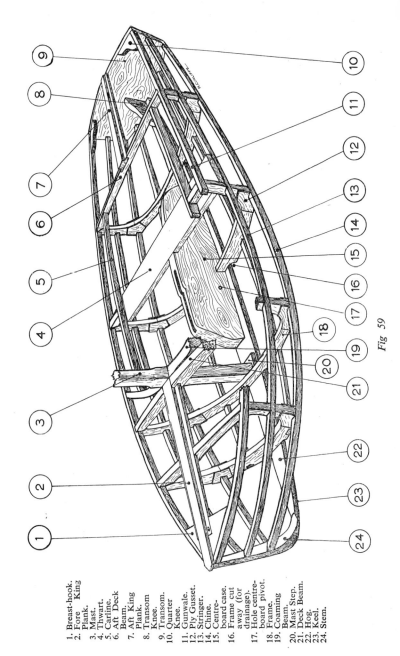

Fig 59

1. Breast-hook.
2. Fore King Plank.
3. Mast.
4. Thwart.
5. Carline.
6. Aft Deck Beam.
7. Aft King Plank.
8. Transom Knee.
9. Transom.
10. Quarter Knee.
11. Gunwale.
12. Ply Gusset.
13. Stringer.
14. Chine.
15. Centre-board case.
16. Frame cut away (for drainage).
17. Hole centre-board pivot.
18. Frame.
19. Coaming Beam.
20. Mast Step.
21. Deck Beam.
22. Hog.
23. Keel.
24. Stern.

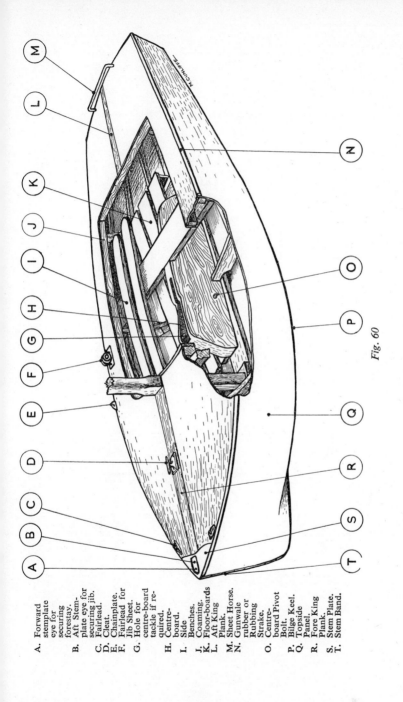

M. C. UNLIFFE.

Fig. 60

A. Forward
   stemplate
   eye for
   securing
   forestay.
B. Aft Stem-
   plate eye for
   securing jib.
C. Fairlead.
D. Cleat.
E. Chainplate.
F. Fairlead for
   Jib Sheet.
G. Hole for
   centre-board
   tackle if re-
   quired.
H. Centre-
   board.
I. Side
   Benches.
J. Coaming.
K. Floor-boards
L. Aft King
   Plank.
M. Sheet Horse.
N. Gunwale
   rubber or
   Rubbing
   Strake.
O. Centre-
   board Pivot
   Bolt.
P. Bilge Keel.
Q. Topside
   Panel.
R. Fore King
   Plank.
S. Stem Plate.
T. Stem Band.

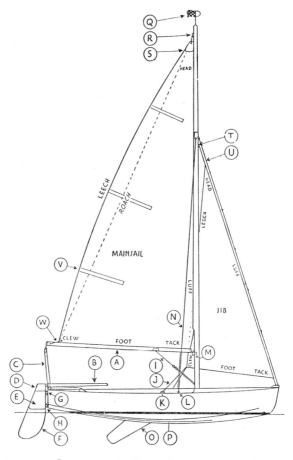

A. Boom.	I. Kicking Strap.	Q. Racing Flag.
B. Tiller.	J. Jib Sheet.	R. Main Halyard.
C. Main Sheet.	K. Jib Sheet Fairlead.	S. Head Board.
D. Tiller Hood.	L. Chainplate.	T. Jib Halyard.
E. Rudder Stock.	M. Gooseneck.	U. Forestay.
F. Rudder Blade.	N. Shrouds.	V. Sail Batten.
G. Top Pintle and Gudgeon.	O. Centre-board.	W. Sail Outhaul.
H. Bottom Pintle and Gudgeon.	P. Bilge Keel.	

Fig. 61

(*Courtesy: Bell Woodworking Co. Ltd*)

LISTS OF CLUBS SAILING PARTICULAR TYPES OF BOATS AND CLASS SECRETARIES

The various Class Association Secretaries have given me lists of clubs sailing their boats as a class, and in some cases I have included clubs that also have owners of a particular boat on their list of members. Where this consideration affects the prospective builder's choice of what type of boat to build I suggest that he writes to the Association Secretary to check up on the latest details. For example, the more recent designs, such as the Enterprise, have a very rapidly growing membership, and more clubs are taking the Enterprise up as their class boat every month.

'YACHTING WORLD' CADET

The Cadet is sailed at something in the region of 200 clubs all over the world, and the *Yachting World* consider that it is advisable for a prospective owner to write to the Association Secretary for up-to-date details.

'Yachting World' Cadet Class Association Secretary,
c/o *Yachting World*,
Dorset House,
Stamford Street, SE1

THE 'LIGHT CRAFT' GRADUATE

The Graduate is sailed by the clubs listed below, and these clubs have reasonable numbers of Graduate owners as members.

Abbey Sailing Club
Avon Sailing Club
Aylesbury Sailing Club
Beeston Sailing Club
Bensons Sailing Club
Blackwater Sailing Club
Cam Sailing Club

Chipstead Sailing Club
Essex Yacht Club
Fairhaven Sailing Club
Felpham Sailing Club
Frensham Pond Sailing Club
G.E.C. Research Sailing Club
Hampton Sailing Club

Kinghorn Yacht Club
Lea Valley Sailing Club
Lowton Sailing Club
Newhaven and Seaford Sailing Club
North Lincs. Sailing Club
Nottingham University Sailing Club
Ruston Sailing Club

South Cerney Sailing Club
Stone Sailing Club
Tamworth Sailing Club
Tower Yacht Club
Welland Yacht Club
Welton Sailing Club
Weybridge Sailing Club
Witham Sailing Club
Yeadon Sailing Club

Hon. Secretary Graduate Class Association,
George Miles,
c/o George Miles Ltd,
94/98 Petty France, SW1

HERON (CARTOP)

The following clubs have Heron classes:

Abbey Sailing Club
Avon Sailing Club
Aylesbury Sailing Club
Bedford Sailing Club
Bellerive Yacht Club (Tasmania)
Bletchley Sailing Club
Blundellsands Sailing Club
Bridge Works Yacht Club
Brighton Sailing Club
Bristol Avon Sailing Club
Chase Sailing Club
Chester Sailing and Cruising Club
Chipstead Sailing Club
Cookham Reach Sailing Club
Dell Quay Sailing Club
Exe Sailing Club
Eyott Sailing Club
Hampton Sailing Club
Hartlepool Sailing Club
Hunts. Sailing Club
Kingston Beach Sailing Club (Tasmania)
Leigh Sailing Club
Lindisfarne Sailing Club (Tasmania)
Loch Earn Sailing Club

Lockheed Sports and Social Club
Loxford School Yacht Club
Lympstone Sailing Club
Medway Yacht Club
Merioneth Yacht Club
Pennington Sailing Club
Perth Sailing Club
Reading Sailing Club
Ribble Cruising Club
Royal Cinque Ports Yacht Club
Royal Hong Kong Yacht Club
Rudyard Lake Sailing Club
Ruislip Lido Sailing Club
South Shields Motor Boat and Yachting Club
Three Counties Sailing Club
Tower Yacht Club
Tranmere Sailing Club
Upriver Sailing Club
Wallasey Yacht Club
West Kirby Sailing Club
Weybridge Sailing Club
Wyre Mill Club (Sailing Section)
Yeadon Sailing Club
Yorkshire Ouse Sailing Club

There are many other clubs that have Heron owners.

Hon. Secretary Heron (Cartop) Class Association,
F. L. Findlay,
18 Eastcote Road,
Ruislip, Middlesex

FLEETWIND ONE-DESIGN

Fleetwinds are sailed by the following clubs:

Bexhill Sailing Club
Bognor Regis Yacht Club
Chipstead Sailing Club
Dover Yacht Club
Hastings and St Leonards Sailing
   Club
Kericho Sailing Club, Kenya
Lea Valley Sailing Club
Maldon Little Ship Club
Marconi Sailing Club, Heybridge

Negombo R.A.F. Sailing Club,
   Ceylon
Oxford University Yacht Club
Rochester Cruising Club
Songwa Sailing Club, Uganda
Thurrock Yacht Club, Grays
Tudor Sailing Club, Portsmouth
Walton and Frinton Yacht Club
Wessex Sailing Club
Wetson Sailing Club

Hon. Secretary Fleetwind Association,
G. A. Young,
41 Chippingfield,
Harlow, Essex

THE OSPREY

The following clubs have adopted the Osprey as a club class:

Mounts Bay Sailing Club, Cornwall
New Quay Sailing Club, Cardiganshire
Sandersfoot Sailing Club, Pembrokeshire

There are Osprey owners in the following clubs:

Barry Sailing Club
Bristol Avon Sailing Club
Fishguard Bay Sailing Club
Hamble River Sailing Club
Horning Sailing Club
Kuwait Dolphin Yacht Club
Lagos Yacht Club
Lyme Regis Yacht Club

Mumbles Yacht Club
Newquay (Cornwall) Yacht Club
Penarth M.B. & S.C.
South Cerney Sailing Club
Trent Valley Sailing Club
Yarmouth and Gorleston Yacht
   Club

Hon. Secretary Osprey Class Owners Association,
Hugh Thomas,
3 Maeshenffordd, Cardigan

THE G.P. FOURTEEN CLASS ASSOCIATION

The following clubs have adopted the G.P. as a racing class:

Air Service Training Sailing Club
Avon Sailing Club
Bassenthwaite Sailing Club
Bedford Sailing Club
Benfleet Yacht Club
Bexhill Sailing Club
Blackpool and Fleetwood Yacht Club
Blundellsands Sailing Club
Bognor Regis Yacht Club
Bolton Sailing Club
Brightlingsea Sailing Club
Broadstairs Sailing Club
Burwain Sailing Club
Carrick Sailing Club
Chase Sailing Club
Clevedon Sailing Club
Combs Sailing Club
Conway Yacht Club
County Antrim Yacht Club
Cyprus District Yacht Club
Dale Yacht Club
Dee Sailing Club
Desborough Sailing Club
Dovey Sailing Club
Filey Sailing Club
Folland Aircraft Sailing Club
Freetown Sailing Club
Frensham Pond Sailing Club
Goring Thames Sailing Club
Gravesend Sailing Club
Hamble River Sailing Club
Hampton Sailing Club
Helensburgh Sailing Club
Hollingworth Sailing Club
Holyhead Sailing Club
Holywood Sailing Club
Hoylake Sailing Club
Kirkcudbright Sailing Club
Lairn Sailing Club
Largs Sailing Club

Laporte Sailing Club
Lawrenny Yacht Club
Leigh Sailing Club
Lockheed Sailing Club
Lympstone Sailing Club
Maithon Yacht Club
Maldon Yacht Club
Manchester Cruising Association
Margate Yacht Club
Middle Nene Cruising Club
Nantwich and Border Counties Yacht Club
New Quay Yacht Club
Northampton Sailing Club
North Belfast Yacht Club
North Wales Cruising Club
Northwich Sailing Club
Penang Swimming Club (Sailing Section)
Penarth M.B. & S.C.
Quoile Sailing Club
Red Wharf Bay Sailing Club
Rhyl Yacht Club
Royal Highland Yacht Club
Royal Northumberland Yacht Club
Royal Singapore Yacht Club
Royal Temple Yacht Club
Royal Windermere Yacht Club
Rugby Sailing Club
Rye Harbour Sailing Club
Sheppey Yacht Club
Shropshire Sailing Club
Southampton Water Sailing Association
South Staffordshire Sailing Club
South Yorkshire Sailing Club
Stone Sailing Club
Swanage Sailing Club
Three Counties Sailing Club
Trearddur Bay Sailing Club

Twickenham Yacht Club
Tynemouth Sailing Club
Wembley Sailing Club

West Cheshire Sailing Club
West Lancashire Yacht Club
West Kirby Sailing Club

Hon. Secretary and Treasurer,
J. E. Austin
38 Lea Road,
Heaton Moor,
Stockport, Cheshire

'NEWS CHRONICLE' ENTERPRISE ASSOCIATION

The following clubs have either adopted or are proposing to adopt the Enterprise as their class boat:

Arun Bay Yacht Club, Littlehampton
Barnt Green Sailing Club, Warwickshire
Birmingham University Sailing Club
Eastbourne Sailing Club
Guernsey Yacht Club

Leigh Sailing Club, Lancashire
Royal Cinque Ports Yacht Club, Dover
Stort Sailing and Canoe Club, Bishop's Stortford
Wraysbury Lake Sailing Club, Buckinghamshire

Hon. Secretary,
A. R. Lanning,
c/o *News Chronicle*,
12–22 Bouverie Street, EC4

NATIONAL FIREFLY ASSOCIATION

Clubs with a fleet of six or more boats

Abbey Sailing Club
Aldenham Sailing Club
Arun Yacht Club
Avon Yacht Club
Banbury Sailing Club
Barnet Green Sailing Club
Bembridge Sailing Club
Bexhill Sailing Club
Blakeney Sailing Club
Bosham Sailing Club
Brancaster Staithe Sailing Club

Bristol Corinthian Yacht Club
Burwain Sailing Club
Cam Sailing Club
Cambridge University Sailing Club
Dartmouth R. N. Club
Dee Sailing Club
Dell Quay Sailing Club
Dover College Sailing Club
Dublin Bay Sailing Club
Emsworth Sailing Club
Felixstowe Sailing Club

Goring-on-Thames Sailing Club
Herne Bay Sailing Club
Hollingworth Lake Sailing Club
Itchenor Sailing Club
Llangorse Sailing Club
London Corinthian
Manchester Cr. Association
Medway Yacht Club
Midlands Sailing Club
Nautical College, Pangbourne
Norfolk Broads Yacht Club
Northwich Sailing Club
Oxford University Yacht Club
Penarth Yacht Club
R.A.F. Sailing Association
Reading University Sailing Club
R.M.A. Sandhurst
Royal Harwich Yacht Club
Royal Lymington Yacht Club
Royal Windermere Yacht Club
Rugby Sailing Club
Shanklin Sailing Club
Shropshire Sailing Club
Smiths of England Sailing Club
Snettisham Beach Sailing Club
Snowflake Sailing Club
South Staffs Sailing Club
Stokes Bay Sailing Club
Sussex Yacht Club
Swanage Sailing Club
Tamesis Club
Thames United Sailing Club
University of London Sailing Club
Waldringfield Sailing Club
Wembley Sailing Club
West Kirby Sailing Club
Whitstable Yacht Club
Yorkshire Ouse Sailing Club

There are nearly one hundred additional clubs that have less than six boats in their fleet, and changes are always taking place. It is therefore wise to write to the secretary for up-to-date information.

Hon. Secretary,
Michael Cook
39 Queens Gate, S.W.7

THE WAYFARER

The Wayfarer has been adopted as a class boat by the Watermouth Yacht Club.

Secretary W. Wrench-Buck, The Cottage, Eastacombe, Barnstaple, Devon.

ADDRESS APPENDIX

Ace Marine (Engines) Ltd, 176 Heath Road, Twickenham, Middlesex. Tel. Popesgrove 5970.

Aero Research Ltd, Duxford, Cambridge. Tel. Sawston 2121.

Ashworth Kirk (Woodwork) Ltd, London Road, Nottingham. Tel. 85081.

Auto Marine Engineers Ltd, The Dock, Lytham, Lancashire. Tel. Lytham 5531.

Baxenden Chemical Co., Ltd, Paragon Works, Baxenden, near Accrington, Lancashire. Tel. Accrington 4631; *and* Clifton House, 83–117 Euston Road, London, NW1. Tel. Euston 6140.

Bell Woodworking Co., Ltd, Narborough Road South, Leicester. Tel. 33251.

Bennett Woodworking (Manchester) Ltd, Alexandra Works, Erskine Street, Manchester, 15. Tel. Moss Side 3381/3.

Beta Marine Ltd, High Street, Emsworth, Hants. Tel. 2354.

H. W. Bone & Co., Ltd, (Marine Division) Colne Engain, Colchester, Essex. Tel. Earls Colne 238.

Black & Decker Ltd, Harmondsworth, Middlesex. Tel. West Drayton 2681/9.

Bowker & Budd Ltd, Bosham, Sussex. Tel. 2149.

S. N. Bridges & Co., Ltd, Bridges Place, Parsons Green Lane, SW6. Tel. Renown 3344.

British Anzani Engineering Co., Ltd, Windmill Road, Hampton Hill, Middlesex. Tel. Molesey 2690/1.

British Seagull Co., Ltd, Fleets Bridge, Poole, Dorset. Tel. 1651.

Brummer Ltd, Oyster Lane, Byfleet, Surrey. Tel. 3636.

Cellon Ltd, Kingston-on-Thames, Surrey. Tel. 1234.

Chamberlains, 94 Gerrard Street, Birmingham 19. Tel. Northern 2193.

Chippendale Boats Ltd, Lower Quay, Fareham, Hants. Tel. 2688; *and* 59 Queens Square, Bristol, 1. Tel. 22429.

Cousland & Browne, Ltd, Piggery Wharf, Manor Farm Road, Alperton, Wembley, Middlesex. Tel. Perivale 6348.

Crevald's Services Ltd, 468 London Road, Langley, Slough, Bucks. Tel. Langley 372.

Cuprinol Ltd, Terminal House, Victoria, London, SW1. Tel. Sloane 9274.

Dee-Craft, Pier Plain, Gorleston-on-Sea, Norfolk. Tel. 1120.

Denton & Partners Ltd, Perimeter Road, The Aerodrome, Woodley, Reading, Berkshire. Tel. Sonning 2412.

Design Boat Co., 1 Ridge Road, Childs Hill, London, NW2. Tel. Hampstead 9893/4.

A. E. Eckford, Bourne Cottage, Broxbourne, Herts. Tel. Hoddesdon 2301.

Evode Ltd, Stafford. Tel. 2241; *and* 1 Victoria Street, London, SW1. Tel. Abbey 4622/3.

Fairey Marine Ltd, Hamble, Hampshire. Tel. 2135.

Fenn & Wood Ltd, Mill Lane, Taplow, Bucks. Tel. Maidenhead 3591.

M. S. Gibb Ltd, Clock Tower Buildings, Warsash, near Southampton, Hants. Tel. Locksheath 3136.

Kenneth M. Gibbs & Co., Ltd, Sandhills, Shepperton, Middlesex. Tel. Walton-on-Thames 926.

Jack Holt Ltd, The Embankment, Putney, London, SW15. Tel. Putney 6256 and 4449.

C. & J. Hampton Ltd, Record Tool Works, Sheffield, 2. Tel. 24076.

International Paints Ltd, Grosvenor Gardens House, London, SW1. Tel. Tate Gallery 7070.

Kitboats, Edinburgh Way, Temple Fields, Harlow, Essex. Tel. 25633.

Light Craft, Link House, Store Street, London, WC1. Tel. Museum 9792.

Leicester, Lovell & Co., Ltd, North Baddesley, Southampton. Tel. Rownhams 363.

R. Moore & Sons (Wroxham) Ltd, Wroxham, Norfolk. Tel. 93.

Raven Boat Co., 206 Mersea Road, Colchester. Tel. 4458.

Richmond Slipways Ltd, Ducks Walk, East Twickenham, Middlesex. Tel. Popesgrove 5062.

F. Ryland (plywood), 107 Pershore Street, Birmingham, 5. Tel. Midland 3053.

Llewellyn Ryland Ltd, Balsall Heath Works, Haben Street, Birmingham, 12. Tel. Calthorpe 2284/6.

Sainter Bros., Ltd, Portwood, Stockport. Tel. 2836/7.

Scotia Marine, Lower Harbour, Perth. Tel. 3469.

Simmonds Aerocessories Ltd, Treforest, Pontypridd, Glamorgan. Tel. Treforest 2211.

Slingsby Sailplanes Ltd, Kirkbymoorside, Yorkshire. Tel. 312/3.

Small Craft, West End, Southampton. Tel. West End 2305.

Stanley Works (Great Britain) Ltd, Sheffield. Tel. 27424.

Stuart Turner Ltd, Henley-on-Thames, Oxon. Tel. 660.

Tormentor Yacht Station Ltd, Stone Pier, Warsash, Hants. Tel. Locks-heath 2357.

Wright & Sons (Ipswich) Ltd, Cullingham Road, Ipswich. Tel. 3871.

Wolf Electrical Tools Ltd, Pioneer Works, Hanger Lane, London, W5. Tel. Perivale 5631/4 and 6421/3.

Wyche & Coppock Ltd, Radford Mill, Norton Street, Nottingham. Tel. 75842.

Yachting Monthly, 3 Clements Inn, London, WC2. Tel. Holborn 5327.

Yachting World, Dorset House, Stamford Street, London, SE1. Tel. Waterloo 3333.

Yachts and Yachting, 21 Cliff Town Road, Southend-on-Sea, Essex. Tel. 45595.

INDEX

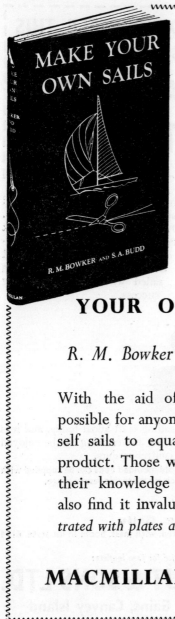

It's even greater fun with Stanley Tools

A Stanley Plane and "Yankee" Spiral Ratchet Screwdriver in use on small boat construction at a recent Lilliput display at Hulton House, London.

The care which goes into building a boat deserves that extra satisfaction which comes from the use of craftsmen's tools—the tools that Stanley make. Their inbred quality gives them that increased efficiency which is so essential to a job well done. Whether for drilling, screwing, planing, boring or smoothing, your tool dealer will have the Stanley Tool you want.

No. 5 Plane 49/9

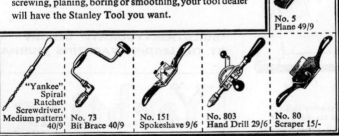

"Yankee" Spiral Ratchet Screwdriver. Medium pattern 40/9

No. 73 Bit Brace 40/9

No. 151 Spokeshave 9/6

No. 803 Hand Drill 29/6

No. 80 Scraper 15/-

Cadet

Heron

Solo

G.P.14

Pioneered to world success

Since YACHTING WORLD pioneered the home building movement with the Yachting World Cadet, many a yachtsman has discovered how inexpensive it is to build from this famous journal's Build-Her-Yourself plans. Today, thousands of expertly designed YACHTING WORLD craft, ranging from the Utility Pram Dinghy to the lively 19-ft. 8-in. sloop 'Light Crest', have been built. Helping the home boat builder is but one mission of YACHTING WORLD. It supplies the most authoritative technical information and advice for all followers of power or sail—for sailing, racing and cruising. Start reading it today!

'BUILD - HER - YOURSELF' DESIGNS
BY THE LEADING YACHTING JOURNAL

London Rowing Club Coaching Launch 'Casamajor'. Designer—Alan H. Buchanan Ltd.
Builder—Tucker Brown & Co. Ltd.

WHY are more Boat Builders, Amateur and Professional, using

'*Aquaply*'?
REGD. TRADE MARK

Healey Marine Ltd.
'Ski-Master'
Builder—
Aqua-Craft Ltd.

BECAUSE 'Aquaply' is a British-made plywood specially developed for boat-building, offering you all the following advantages:—

Specification conforms to the revised BSS 1088—1957.

Weather and Boil-Proof bonding (BSS 1203 WBP).

Face veneers of carefully selected Utile/Sapele.

High strength/weight ratio.

Immediate delivery ex-stock.

William Mallinson
and Sons Ltd.
TIMBER and VENEER MERCHANTS

130-150 HACKNEY ROAD · LONDON · E.2

Telephone: Shoreditch 7654 (15 lines)   Telegrams: "Almoner," London
MANUFACTURERS OF PLYWOOD, 'ARMOURPLY', PANELS,
COMPOSITE PARTITIONING AND INFILL PANELS

STUART

MARINE ENGINES

PUMPS

LIGHTING PLANTS

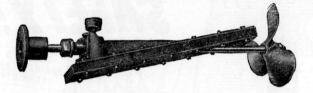

The Stuart Adjustable Metal Shaft Log

Stuart engines are supplied with a complete set of stern-gear and installation equipment—everything down to the smallest items such as petrol pipe clips! Apart from the standard fittings, which suit the majority of hulls, there are special alternatives, such as this shaft log.

The shaft log is a most useful fitting for the boatbuilder, whether amateur or professional. It saves the need for boring an accurate sterntube hole and, used with a Stuart adjustable 'A' bracket, simplifies installation enormously.

If you are building a boat for which an engine of 1½ to 8 b.h.p. is suitable we suggest you consult us, asking for the 36-page catalogue No. 1610.

STUART TURNER LTD.
HENLEY-ON-THAMES, OXON:
TEL: 660

SHELL
COUNTY
GUIDES

Edited by John Betjeman

POCKET PILOT FOR THE SOUTH COAST
K. Adlard Coles

From all booksellers at 12/6 each
Published by Faber & Faber Ltd